A Year of Mystery Coordinate Graphs

By: Didi DeBoer
& Meg Pfent

Printed in the United States of America

ISBN 13: 978-1-71149-425-8

4750 Venture Drive, Ste 400
Ann Arbor, MI 48108
800.218.5971
www.xanedu.com

contents

Teacher Directions

Students will enjoy completing this engaging math activity as they plot ordered pairs and reveal fun mystery pictures. Grid paper and coordinate points (first quadrant for all positive whole numbers or four-quadrant for practice with positive and negative whole numbers) are provided and ready to use. This activity is great for math centers, home schooling, fast finishers, or homework. Students love to complete and color these pictures and they make a great display in the hallway or on a bulletin board, especially when mounted on colorful construction paper.

Student Instructions

Plot the ordered pairs and connect using straight lines as you plot. When you reach the word "**STOP**" you have reached the last point for that area of the picture. Once each area is completed the mystery picture will be revealed! Color each picture with colored pencils or crayons so that the color doesn't go through to the next page. Have Fun!

WINTER MYSTERY PICTURE #1 (FIRST QUADRANT)

Plot the ordered pairs, connecting with straight lines as you go. Be sure to stop when you reach **"STOP"** and begin a new series of connected lines at each **"START"**. *Have fun!*

START
(5, 22)
(2, 22)
(0, 20)
(2, 18)
(7, 18)
(14, 11)
(19, 11)
(24, 16)
(24, 23)
(19, 28)
(22, 31)
(22, 34)
(19, 34)
(15, 30)
(11, 34)
(6, 34)
(2, 30)
(2, 25)
(5, 22)
STOP

START
(14, 11)
(14, 9)
(13, 9)
(12, 8)
(12, 6)
(19, 6)
(19, 11)
STOP

START
(24, 18)
(26, 18)
(26, 17)
(27, 16)
(29, 16)
(29, 23)
(24, 23)
STOP

START
(7, 23)
(3, 27)
(3, 30)
(4, 31)
(5, 31)
(5, 32)
(6, 33)
(9, 33)
(13, 29)
STOP

START
(4, 23)
(9, 23)
(13, 27)
(13, 32)
STOP

START
(5, 22)
(6, 21)
(10, 21)
(15, 26)
(15, 30)
STOP

START
(9, 21)
(16, 14)
(19, 14)
(22, 17)
(22, 20)
(15, 27)
STOP

START
(10, 21)
(15, 16)
(17, 18)
(12, 23)
STOP

START
(15, 16)
(16, 15)
STOP

START
(16, 17)
(17, 16)
STOP

START
(17, 18)
(18, 17)
STOP

START
(12, 5)
(14, 5)
(14, 6)
(14, 5)
(17, 5)
(17, 6)
(17, 5)
(19, 5)
STOP

START
(30, 23)
(30, 21)
(29, 21)
(30, 21)
(30, 18)
(29, 18)
(30, 18)
(30, 16)
STOP

START
(6, 27)
(6, 28)
(7, 28)
(7, 27)
(5, 27)
(5, 29)
(7, 29)
(7, 28)
STOP

START
(8, 29)
(8, 30)
(9, 30)
(9, 29)
(7, 29)
(7, 31)
(9, 31)
(9, 30)
STOP

START
(8, 25)
(8, 28)
(11, 28)
(11, 25)
(8, 25)
(11, 28)
STOP

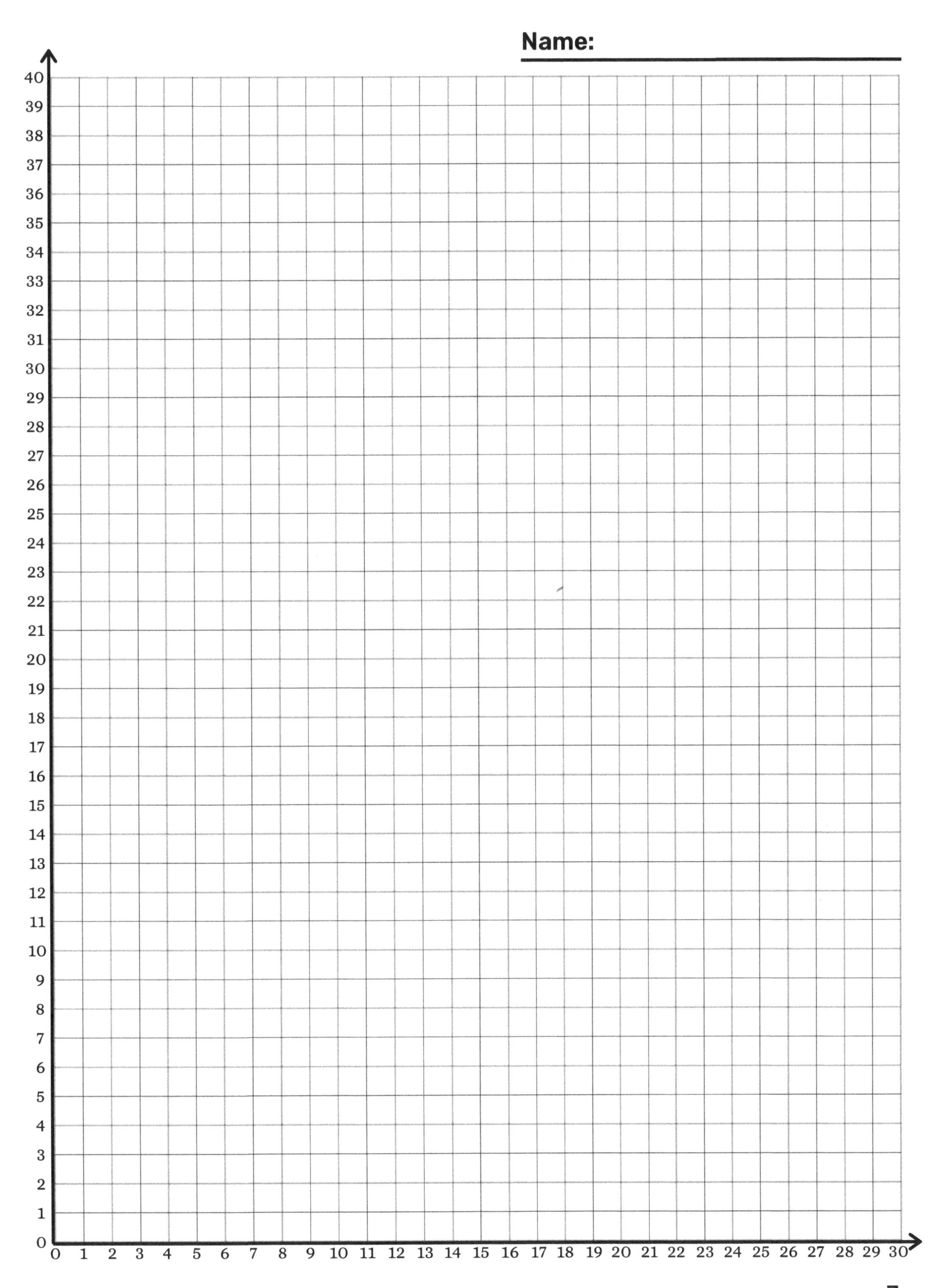
Name:
40 39 38 37 36 35 34 33 32 31 30 29 28 27 26 25 24 23 22 21 20 19 18 17 16 15 14 13 12 11 10 9 8 7 6 5 4 3 2 1 0
0 1 2 3 4 5 6 7 8 9 10 11 12 13 14 15 16 17 18 19 20 21 22 23 24 25 26 27 28 29 30

WINTER MYSTERY PICTURE #1 (FOUR QUADRANT)

Plot the ordered pairs, connecting with straight lines as you go. Be sure to stop when you reach **"STOP"** and begin a new series of connected lines at each **"START"**. *Have fun!*

START
(-10, 2)
(-13, 2)
(-15, 0)
(-13, -2)
(-8, -2)
(-1, -9)
(4, -9)
(9, -4)
(9, 3)
(4, 8)
(7, 11)
(7, 14)
(4, 14)
(0, 10)
(-4, 14)
(-9, 14)
(-13, 10)
(-13, 5)
(-10, 2)
STOP

START
(-1, -9)
(-1, -11)
(-2, -11)
(-3, -12)
(-3, -14)
(4, -14)
(4, -9)
STOP

START
(9, -2)
(11, -2)
(11, -3)
(12, -4)
(14, -4)
(14, 3)
(9, 3)
STOP

START
(-8, 3)
(-12, 7)
(-12, 10)
(-11, 11)
(-10, 11)
(-10, 12)
(-9, 13)
(-6, 13)
(-2, 9)
STOP

START
(-11, 3)
(-6, 3)
(-2, 7)
(-2, 12)
STOP

START
(-10, 2)
(-9, 1)
(-5, 1)
(0, 6)
(0, 10)
STOP

START
(-6, 1)
(1, -6)
(4, -6)
(7, -3)
(7, 0)
(0, 7)
STOP

START
(-5, 1)
(0, -4)
(2, -2)
(-3, 3)
STOP

START
(0, -4)
(1, -5)
STOP

START
(1, -3)
(2, -4)
STOP

START
(2, -2)
(3, -3)
STOP

START
(-3, -15)
(-1, -15)
(-1, -14)
(-1, -15)
(2, -15)
(2, -14)
(2, -15)
(4, -15)
STOP

START
(15, 3)
(15, 1)
(14, 1)
(15, 1)
(15, -2)
(14, -2)
(15, -2)
(15, -4)
STOP

START
(-9, 7)
(-9, 8)
(-8, 8)
(-8, 7)
(-10, 7)
(-10, 9)
(-8, 9)
(-8, 8)
STOP

START
(-7, 9)
(-7, 10)
(-6, 10)
(-6, 9)
(-8, 9)
(-8, 11)
(-6, 11)
(-6, 10)
STOP

START
(-7, 5)
(-7, 8)
(-4, 8)
(-4, 5)
(-7, 5)
(-4, 8)
STOP

Name: ____________________

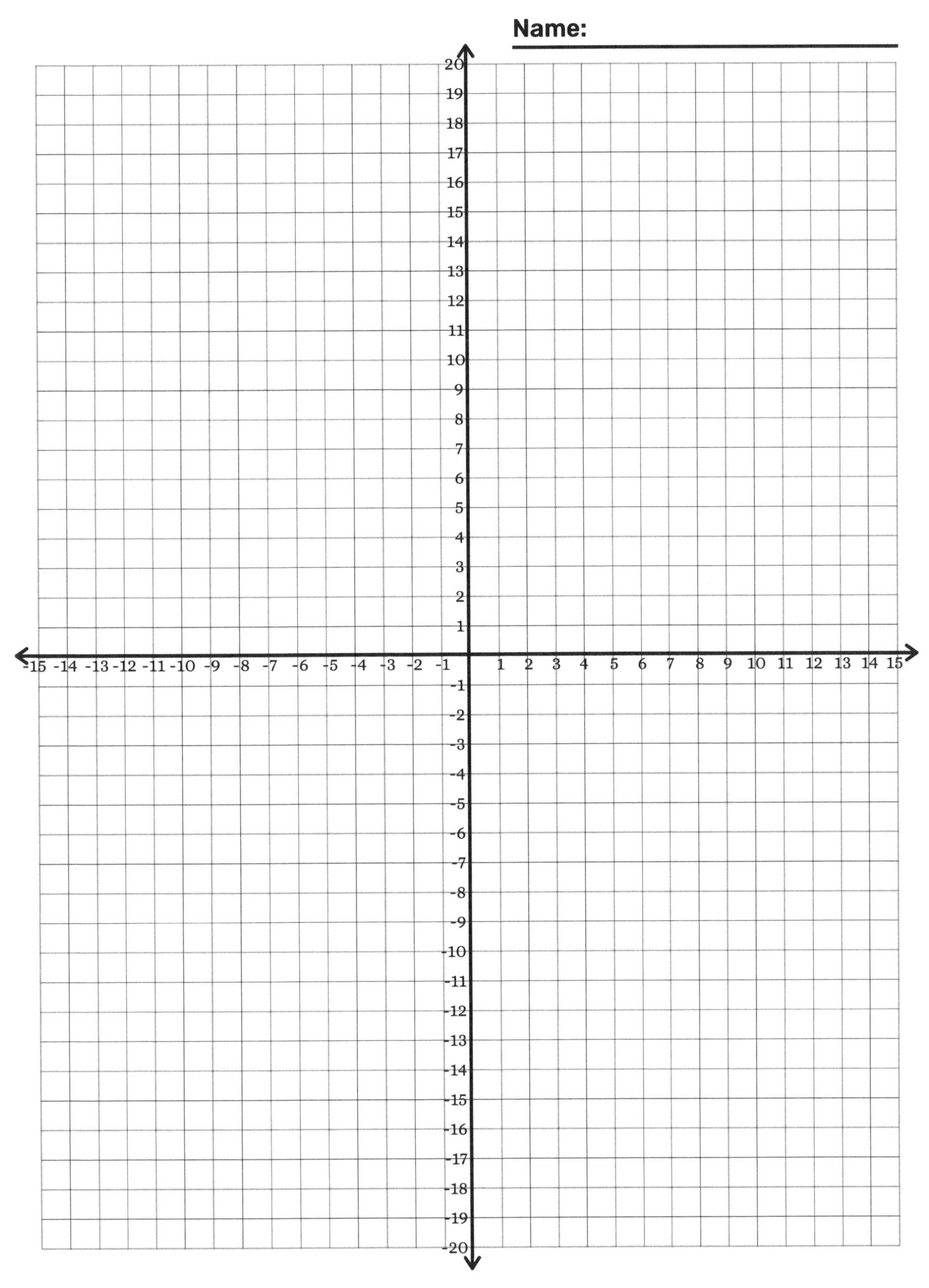
20
19
18
17
16
15
14
13
12
11
10
9
8
7
6
5
4
3
2
1
-15 -14 -13 -12 -11 -10 -9 -8 -7 -6 -5 -4 -3 -2 -1
1 2 3 4 5 6 7 8 9 10 11 12 13 14 15
-1
-2
-3
-4
-5
-6
-7
-8
-9
-10
-11
-12
-13
-14
-15
-16
-17
-18
-19
-20

WINTER MYSTERY PICTURE #2
(FIRST QUADRANT)

Plot the ordered pairs, connecting with straight lines as you go. Be sure to stop when you reach **"STOP"** and begin a new series of connected lines at each **"START"**. *Have fun!*

START
(9, 21)
(7, 23)
(7, 31)
(11, 35)
(19, 35)
(23, 31)
(23, 23)
(21, 21)
(9, 21)
STOP

START
(8, 22)
(8, 19)
(9, 18)
(21, 18)
(22, 19)
(22, 22)
STOP

START
(8, 20)
(7, 19)
(7, 2)
(8, 1)
(12, 1)
(13, 2)
(13, 14)
(13, 3)
(17, 3)
(17, 14)
(17, 2)
(18, 1)
(22, 1)
(23, 2)
(23, 19)
(22, 20)
STOP

START
(7, 13)
(3, 9)
(2, 9)
(0, 7)
(0, 3)
(2, 1)
(5, 1)
(7, 3)
(7, 7)
(5, 9)
(3, 9)
STOP

START
(2, 8)
(1, 7)
(1, 3)
(2, 2)
(5, 2)
(6, 3)
(6, 7)
(5, 8)
(2, 8)
STOP

START
(23, 13)
(27, 9)
(28, 9)
(30, 7)
(30, 3)
(28, 1)
(25, 1)
(23, 3)
(23, 7)
(25, 9)
(27, 9)
STOP

START
(28, 8)
(29, 7)
(29, 3)
(28, 2)
(25, 2)
(24, 3)
(24, 7)
(25, 8)
(28, 8)
STOP

START
(18, 18)
(18, 8)
(18, 9)
(19, 9)
(19, 8)
(19, 9)
(20, 9)
(20, 8)
(20, 9)
(21, 9)
(21, 8)
(21, 18)
STOP

START
(11, 29)
(11, 31)
(13, 31)
(13, 29)
(11, 29)
(10, 30)
(10, 32)
(11, 33)
(13, 33)
(14, 32)
(14, 30)
(13, 29)
STOP

START
(17, 29)
(17, 31)
(19, 31)
(19, 29)
(17, 29)
(16, 30)
(16, 32)
(17, 33)
(19, 33)
(20, 32)
(20, 30)
(19, 29)
STOP

START
(13, 22)
(11, 24)
(11, 26)
(13, 28)
(17, 28)
(19, 26)
(19, 24)
(17, 22)
(13, 22)
STOP

START
(12, 24)
(13, 23)
(14, 23)
(15, 24)
(15, 25)
(14, 25)
(13, 26)
(13, 27)
(17, 27)
(17, 26)
(16, 25)
(15, 25)
(15, 24)
(16, 23)
(17, 23)
(18, 24)
STOP

START
(7, 30)
(6, 30)
(5, 31)
(5, 34)
(9, 38)
(21, 38)
(25, 34)
(25, 31)
(24, 30)
(23, 30)
(23, 35)
(24, 35)
(23, 35)
(21, 37)
(9, 37)
(7, 35)
(6, 35)
(7, 35)
(7, 30)
STOP

START
(8, 32)
(7, 33)
(7, 35)
(8, 36)
(10, 36)
(11, 35)
STOP

START
(9, 33)
(8, 34)
(9, 35)
(10, 34)
STOP

START
(19, 35)
(20, 36)
(22, 36)
(23, 35)
(23, 33)
(22, 32)
STOP

START
(20, 34)
(21, 35)
(22, 34)
(21, 33)
STOP

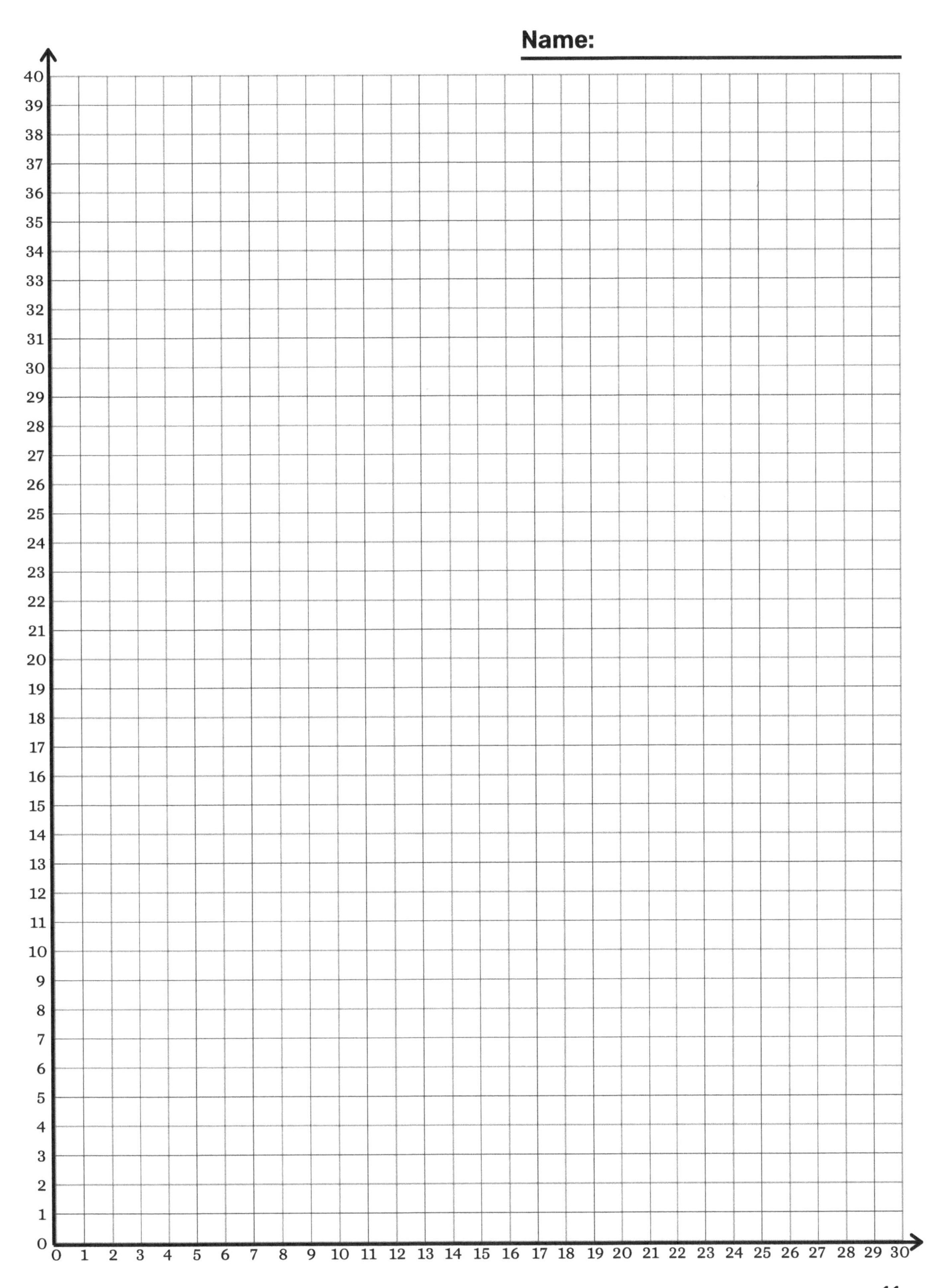
Name:

WINTER MYSTERY PICTURE #2 (FOUR QUADRANT)

Plot the ordered pairs, connecting with straight lines as you go. Be sure to stop when you reach **"STOP"** and begin a new series of connected lines at each **"START"**. *Have fun!*

START
(-6, 1)
(-8, 3)
(-8, 11)
(-4, 15)
(4, 15)
(8, 11)
(8, 3)
(6, 1)
(-6, 1)
STOP

START
(-7, 2)
(-7, -1)
(-6, -2)
(6, -2)
(7, -1)
(7, 2)
STOP

START
(-7, 0)
(-8, -1)
(-8, -18)
(-7, -19)
(-3, -19)
(-2, -18)
(-2, -6)
(-2, -17)
(2, -17)
(2, -6)
(2, -18)
(3, -19)
(7, -19)
(8, -18)
(8, -1)
(7, 0)
STOP

START
(-8, -7)
(-12, -11)
(-13, -11)
(-15, -13)
(-15, -17)
(-13, -19)
(-10, -19)
(-8, -17)
(-8, -13)
(-10, -11)
(-12, -11)
STOP

START
(-13, -12)
(-14, -13)
(-14, -17)
(-13, -18)
(-10, -18)
(-9, -17)
(-9, -13)
(-10, -12)
(-13, -12)
STOP

START
(8, -7)
(12, -11)
(13, -11)
(15, -13)
(15, -17)
(13, -19)
(10, -19)
(8, -17)
(8, -13)
(10, -11)
(12, -11)
STOP

START
(13, -12)
(14, -13)
(14, -17)
(13, -18)
(10, -18)
(9, -17)
(9, -13)
(10, -12)
(13, -12)
STOP

START
(3, -2)
(3, -12)
(3, -11)
(4, -11)
(4, -12)
(4, -11)
(5, -11)
(5, -12)
(5, -11)
(6, -11)
(6, -12)
(6, -2)
STOP

START
(-4, 9)
(-4, 11)
(-2, 11)
(-2, 9)
(-4, 9)
(-5, 10)
(-5, 12)
(-4, 13)
(-2, 13)
(-1, 12)
(-1, 10)
(-2, 9)
STOP

START
(2, 9)
(2, 11)
(4, 11)
(4, 9)
(2, 9)
(1, 10)
(1, 12)
(2, 13)
(4, 13)
(5, 12)
(5, 10)
(4, 9)
STOP

START
(-2, 2)
(-4, 4)
(-4, 6)
(-2, 8)
(2, 8)
(4, 6)
(4, 4)
(2, 2)
(-2, 2)
STOP

START
(-3, 4)
(-2, 3)
(-1, 3)
(0, 4)
(0, 5)
(-1, 5)
(-2, 6)
(-2, 7)
(2, 7)
(2, 6)
(1, 5)
(0, 5)
(0, 4)
(1, 3)
(2, 3)
(3, 4)
STOP

START
(-8, 10)
(-9, 10)
(-10, 11)
(-10, 14)
(-6, 18)
(6, 18)
(10, 14)
(10, 11)
(9, 10)
(8, 10)
(8, 15)
(9, 15)
(8, 15)
(6, 17)
(-6, 17)
(-8, 15)
(-9, 15)
(-8, 15)
(-8, 11)
STOP

START
(-7, 12)
(-8, 13)
(-8, 15)
(-7, 16)
(-5, 16)
(-4, 15)
STOP

START
(-6, 13)
(-7, 14)
(-6, 15)
(-5, 14)
STOP

START
(4, 15)
(5, 16)
(7, 16)
(8, 15)
(8, 13)
(7, 12)
STOP

START
(5, 14)
(6, 15)
(7, 14)
(6, 13)
STOP

Name: ____________________

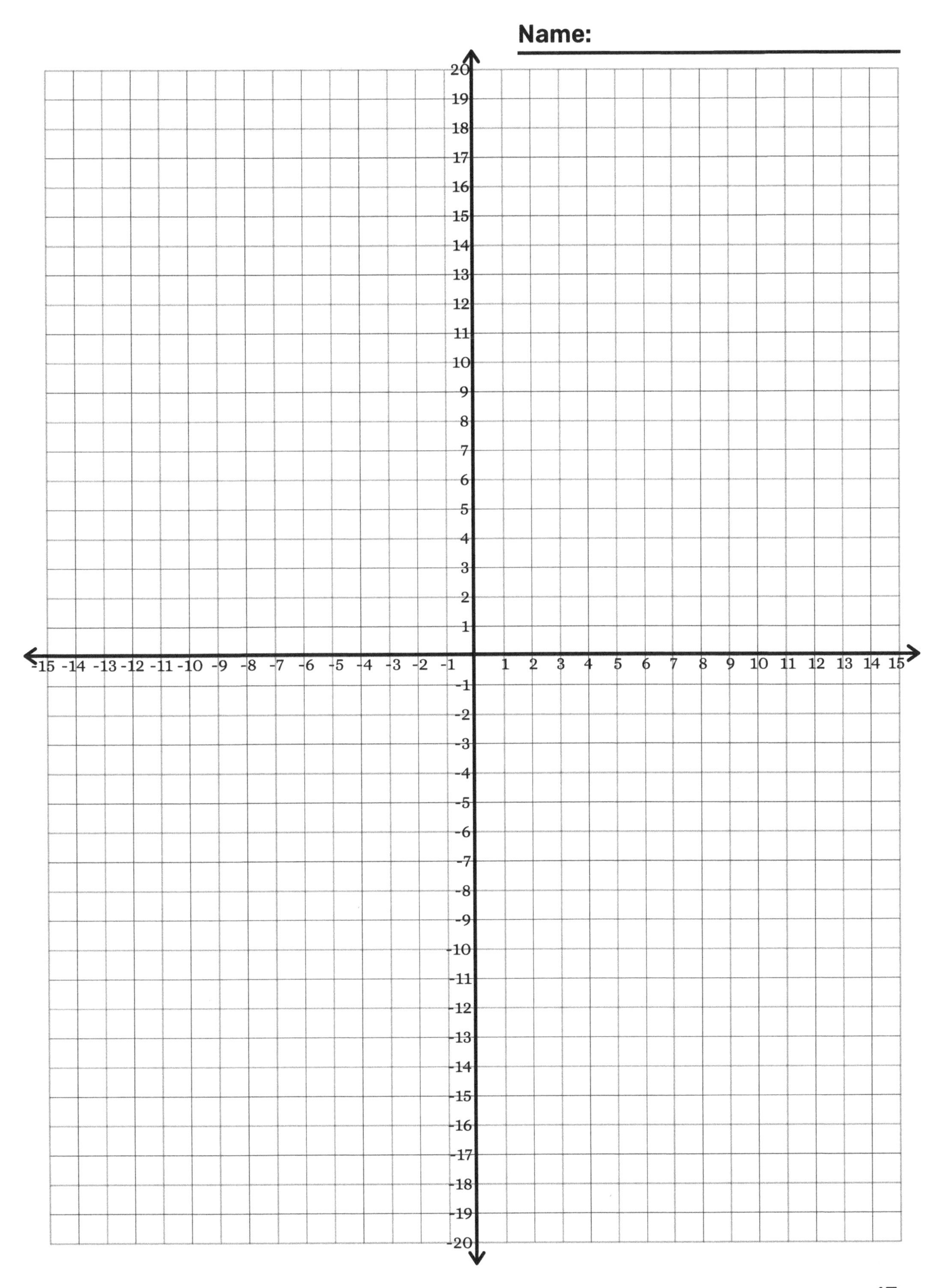

20
19
18
17
16
15
14
13
12
11
10
9
8
7
6
5
4
3
2
1
-15 -14 -13 -12 -11 -10 -9 -8 -7 -6 -5 -4 -3 -2 -1
1 2 3 4 5 6 7 8 9 10 11 12 13 14 15
-1
-2
-3
-4
-5
-6
-7
-8
-9
-10
-11
-12
-13
-14
-15
-16
-17
-18
-19
-20

VALENTINE'S DAY MYSTERY PICTURE #1 (FIRST QUADRANT)

Plot the ordered pairs, connecting with straight lines as you go. Be sure to stop when you reach **"STOP"** and begin a new series of connected lines at each **"START"**. *Have fun!*

<table>
<tr>
<td>**START**
(16, 2)
(16, 3)
(25, 3)
(25, 8)
(24, 9)
(22, 9)
(21, 8)
(21, 9)
(27, 15)
(27, 19)
(25, 21)
(21, 21)
(19, 19)
(19, 17)
(19, 19)
(17, 21)
(16, 21)
(16, 23)
(19, 23)
(22, 26)
(22, 33)
(19, 36)
(10, 36)
(7, 33)
(7, 26)
(10, 23)
(13, 23)
(13, 21)
(12, 20)
(7, 20)
(2, 15)
(2, 8)
(7, 3)
(9, 3)
(10, 2)
(16, 2)
STOP</td>
<td>**START**
(13, 32)
(11, 32)
(11, 33)
(13, 33)
(13, 30)
(11, 30)
(11, 32)
STOP
START
(16, 32)
(18, 32)
(18, 33)
(16, 33)
(16, 30)
(18, 30)
(18, 32)
STOP
START
(13, 23)
(16, 23)
STOP
START
(13, 21)
(16, 21)
STOP
START
(10, 27)
(10, 28)
(9, 28)
(9, 27)
(10, 27)
(12, 25)
(17, 25)
(19, 27)
(20, 27)</td>
<td>(20, 28)
(19, 28)
(19, 27)
STOP
START
(12, 20)
(11, 19)
(11, 15)
(12, 14)
(14, 14)
(15, 13)
(15, 11)
(14, 10)
(12, 10)
(7, 15)
(9, 17)
(11, 15)
STOP
START
(26, 14)
(27, 13)
(25, 11)
(24, 12)
STOP
START
(15, 11)
(19, 7)
(21, 9)
(21, 6)
(22, 6)
(21, 6)
(18, 3)
(16, 3)
(16, 7)
(21, 7)
STOP</td>
<td>**START**
(10, 20)
(5, 15)
(5, 10)
(3, 12)
(3, 10)
(5, 10)
(5, 8)
(7, 6)
(5, 6)
(7, 4)
(7, 6)
(10, 3)
(9, 3)
STOP
START
(5, 18)
(7, 18)
(5, 16)
(5, 18)
STOP
START
(2, 15)
(4, 15)
(4, 13)
(2, 13)
STOP
START
(2, 9)
(4, 9)
(4, 7)
(3, 7)
STOP</td>
<td>**START**
(8, 18)
(11, 18)
STOP
START
(5, 12)
(10, 12)
STOP
START
(6, 7)
(12, 7)
(13, 8)
(15, 8)
(16, 7)
STOP
START
(12, 7)
(12, 5)
(10, 5)
(13, 5)
STOP
DOT AT EACH COORDINATE:
(12, 31)
(17, 31)</td>
</tr>
</table>

Name:

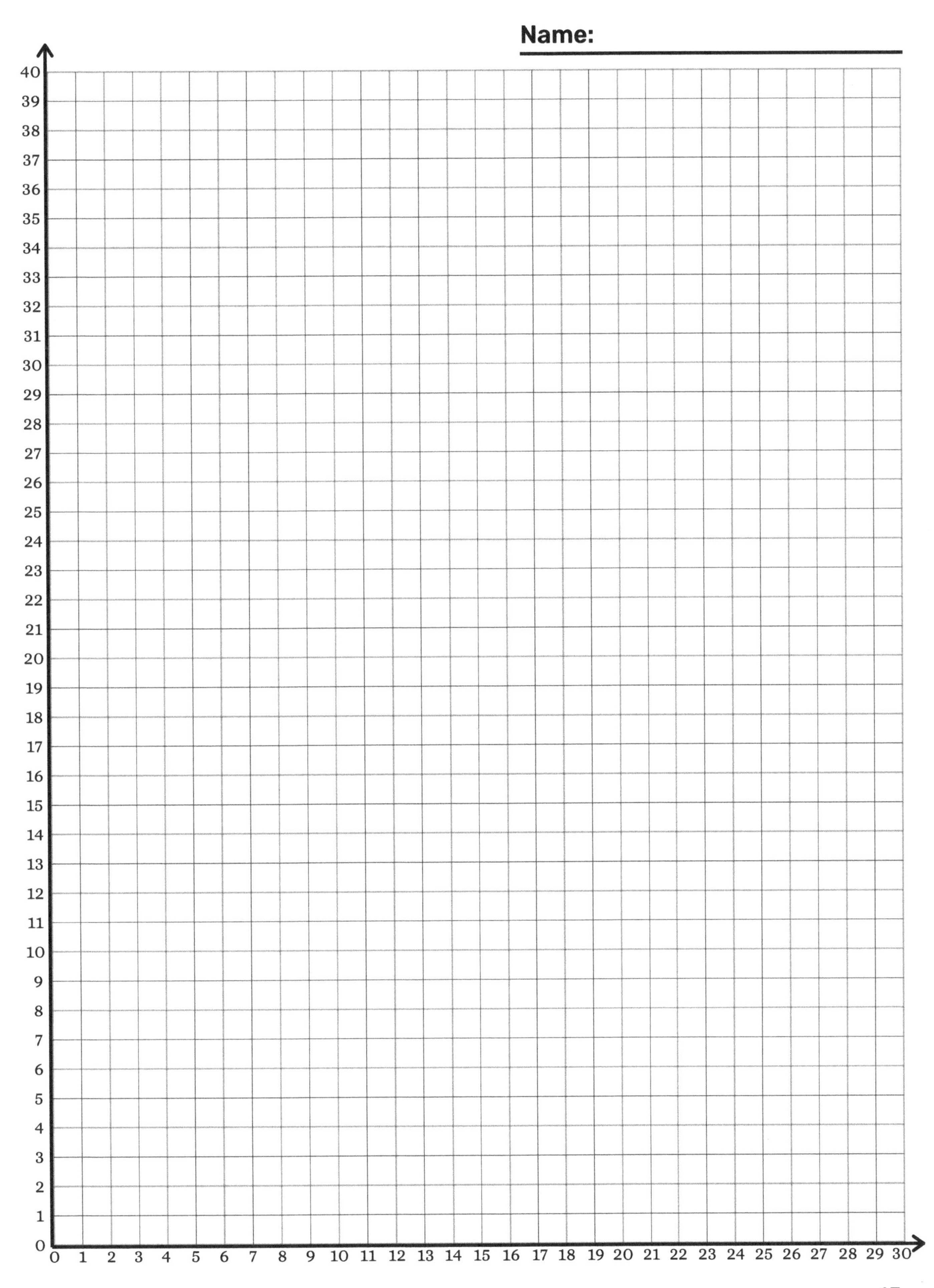
40 39 38 37 36 35 34 33 32 31 30 29 28 27 26 25 24 23 22 21 20 19 18 17 16 15 14 13 12 11 10 9 8 7 6 5 4 3 2 1 0
0 1 2 3 4 5 6 7 8 9 10 11 12 13 14 15 16 17 18 19 20 21 22 23 24 25 26 27 28 29 30

VALENTINE'S DAY MYSTERY PICTURE #1 (FOUR QUADRANT)

Plot the ordered pairs, connecting with straight lines as you go. Be sure to stop when you reach **"STOP"** and begin a new series of connected lines at each **"START"**. *Have fun!*

START
(1, -18)
(1, -17)
(10, -17)
(10, -12)
(9, -11)
(7, -11)
(6, -12)
(6, -11)
(12, -5)
(12, -1)
(10, 1)
(6, 1)
(4, -1)
(4, -3)
(4, -1)
(2, 1)
(1, 1)
(1, 3)
(4, 3)
(7, 6)
(7, 13)
(4, 16)
(-5, 16)
(-8, 13)
(-8, 6)
(-5, 3)
(-2, 3)
(-2, 1)
(-3, 0)
(-8, 0)
(-13, -5)
(-13, -12)
(-8, -17)
(-6, -17)
(-5, -18)
(1, -18)
STOP

START
(-2, 12)
(-4, 12)
(-4, 13)
(-2, 13)
(-2, 10)
(-4, 10)
(-4, 12)
STOP

START
(1, 12)
(3, 12)
(3, 13)
(1, 13)
(1, 10)
(3, 10)
(3, 12)
STOP

START
(-2, 3)
(1, 3)
STOP

START
(-2, 1)
(1, 1)
STOP

START
(-5, 7)
(-5, 8)
(-6, 8)
(-6, 7)
(-5, 7)
(-3, 5)
(2, 5)
(4, 7)
(5, 7)
(5, 8)
(4, 8)
(4, 7)
STOP

START
(-3, 0)
(-4, -1)
(-4, -5)
(-3, -6)
(-1, -6)
(0, -7)
(0, -9)
(-1, -10)
(-3, -10)
(-8, -5)
(-6, -3)
(-4, -5)
STOP

START
(11, -6)
(12, -7)
(10, -9)
(9, -8)
STOP

START
(0, -9)
(4, -13)
(6, -11)
(6, -14)
(7, -14)
(6, -14)
(3, -17)
(1, -17)
(1, -13)
(6, -13)
STOP

START
(-5, 0)
(-10, -5)
(-10, -10)
(-12, -8)
(-12, -10)
(-10, -10)
(-10, -12)
(-8, -14)
(-10, -14)
(-8, -16)
(-8, -14)
(-5, -17)
(-6, -17)
STOP

START
(-10, -2)
(-8, -2)
(-10, -4)
(-10, -2)
STOP

START
(-13, -5)
(-11, -5)
(-11, -7)
(-13, -7)
STOP

START
(-13, -11)
(-11, -11)
(-11, -13)
(-12, -13)
STOP

START
(-7, -2)
(-4, -2)
STOP

START
(-10, -8)
(-5, -8)
STOP

START
(-9, -13)
(-3, -13)
(-2, -12)
(0, -12)
(1, -13)
STOP

START
(-3, -13)
(-3, -15)
(-5, -15)
(-2, -15)
STOP

DOT AT EACH COORDINATE:
(-3, 11)
(2, 11)

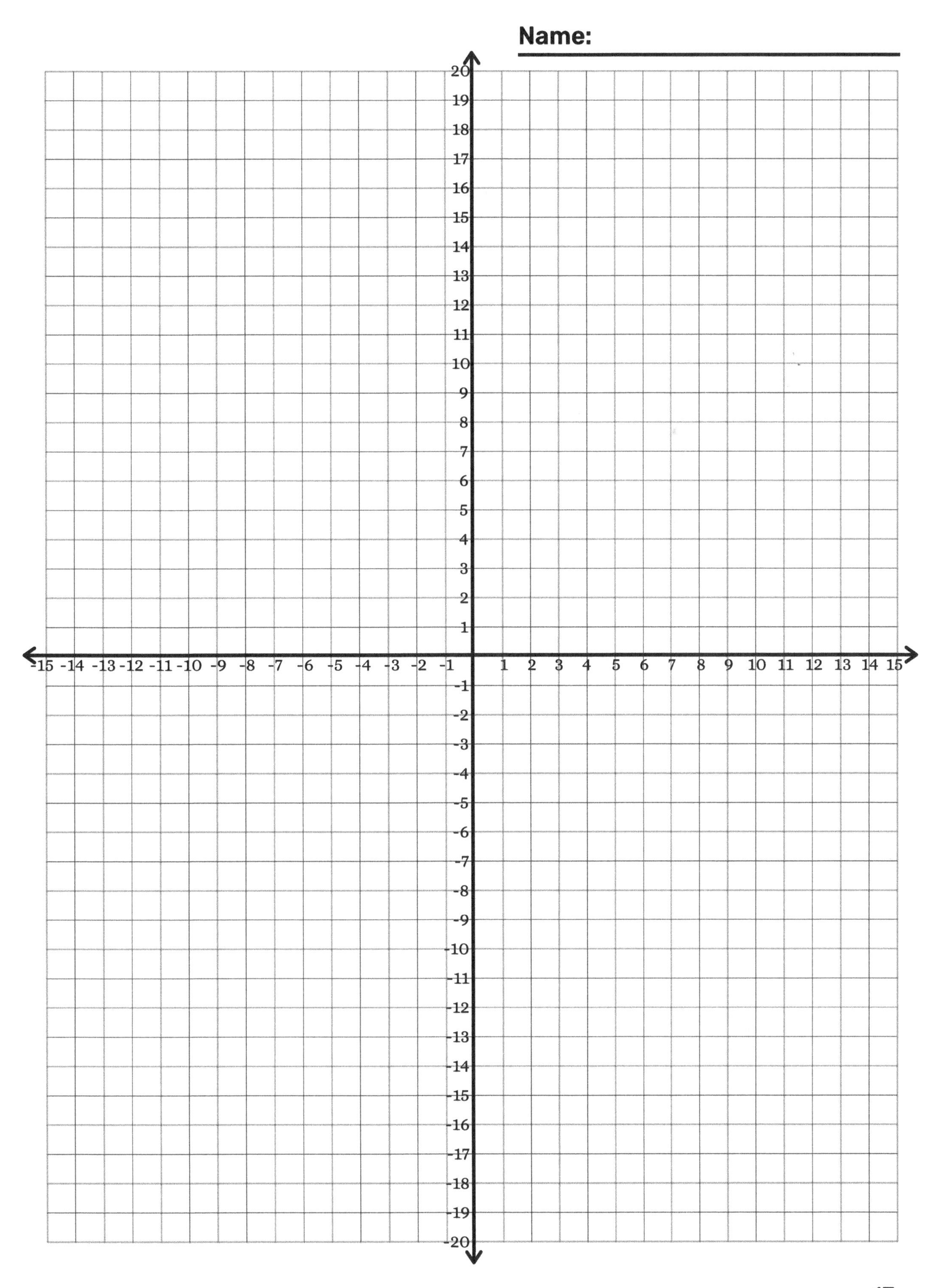
Name:
20 19 18 17 16 15 14 13 12 11 10 9 8 7 6 5 4 3 2 1
-15 -14 -13 -12 -11 -10 -9 -8 -7 -6 -5 -4 -3 -2 -1 1 2 3 4 5 6 7 8 9 10 11 12 13 14 15
-1 -2 -3 -4 -5 -6 -7 -8 -9 -10 -11 -12 -13 -14 -15 -16 -17 -18 -19 -20

VALENTINE'S DAY MYSTERY PICTURE #2 (FIRST QUADRANT)

Plot the ordered pairs, connecting with straight lines as you go. Be sure to stop when you reach **"STOP"** and begin a new series of connected lines at each **"START"**. *Have fun!*

<table>
<tr>
<td>**START**
(8, 30)
(3, 35)
(3, 38)
(4, 39)
(6, 39)
(8, 37)
(10, 39)
(12, 39)
(13, 38)
(13, 35)
(8, 30)
(8, 16)
(11, 13)
(10, 12)
(10, 11)
(13, 11)
(13, 17)
(15, 19)
(14, 20)
(11, 17)
(11, 13)
STOP

START
(12,11)
(12, 9)
(11, 8)
STOP</td>
<td>**START**
(14, 20)
(13, 21)
(13, 25)
(15, 27)
(14, 28)
(14, 30)
(15, 31)
(17, 31)
(18, 30)
(18, 29)
(20, 29)
(20, 30)
(21, 31)
(23, 31)
(24, 30)
(24, 28)
(23, 27)
(25, 25)
(25, 21)
(23, 19)
(25, 17)
(25, 10)
(23, 8)
(15, 8)
(13, 10)
(13, 11)
STOP</td>
<td>**START**
(18, 29)
(18, 28)
(17, 27)
(17, 29)
(15, 29)
(15, 27)
(17, 27)
STOP

START
(20, 29)
(20, 28)
(21, 27)
(21, 29)
(23, 29)
(23, 27)
(21, 27)
STOP

START
(18, 26)
STOP

START
(20, 26)
STOP

START
(15, 19)
(23, 19)
STOP</td>
<td>**START**
(16, 23)
(17, 22)
(21, 22)
(22, 23)
STOP

START
(15, 23)
(17, 23)
STOP

START
(21, 23)
(23, 23)
STOP

START
(24, 20)
(27, 17)
(27, 13)
(28, 12)
(28, 11)
(25, 11)
STOP</td>
<td>**START**
(15, 8)
(15, 3)
(14, 2)
(14, 1)
(18, 1)
(18, 2)
(17, 3)
(17, 8)
STOP

START
(21, 8)
(21, 3)
(20, 2)
(20, 1)
(24, 1)
(24, 2)
(23, 3)
(23, 8)
STOP</td>
</tr>
</table>

Name: ____________________

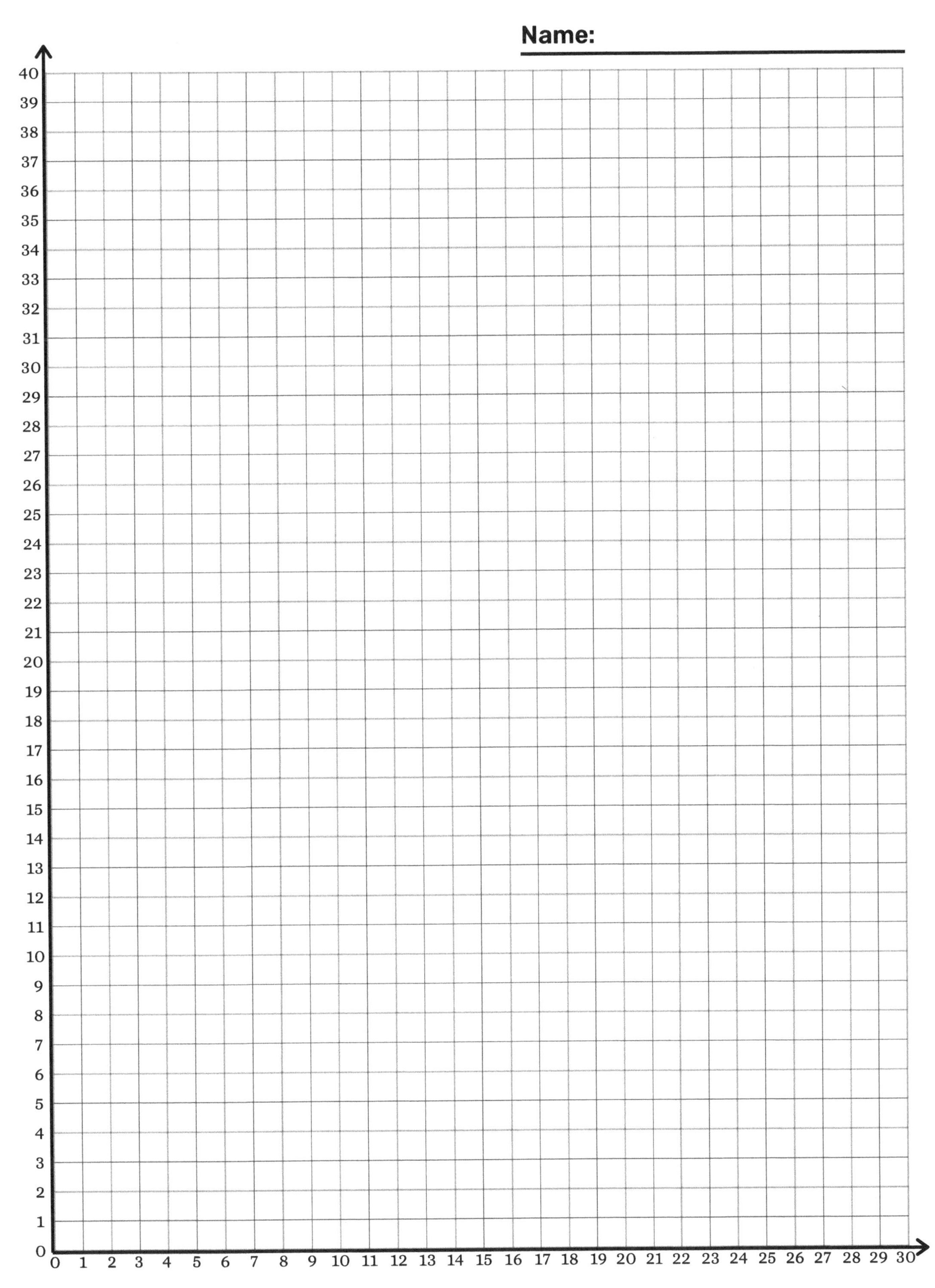

0 1 2 3 4 5 6 7 8 9 10 11 12 13 14 15 16 17 18 19 20 21 22 23 24 25 26 27 28 29 30
0 1 2 3 4 5 6 7 8 9 10 11 12 13 14 15 16 17 18 19 20 21 22 23 24 25 26 27 28 29 30 31 32 33 34 35 36 37 38 39 40

VALENTINE'S DAY MYSTERY PICTURE #2 (FOUR QUADRANT)

Plot the ordered pairs, connecting with straight lines as you go. Be sure to stop when you reach **"STOP"** and begin a new series of connected lines at each **"START"**. *Have fun!*

START	**START**	**START**	**START**	**START**
(-7, 10)	(-1, 0)	(3, 9)	(1, 3)	(0, -12)
(-12, 15)	(-2, 1)	(3, 8)	(2, 2)	(0, -17)
(-12, 18)	(-2, 5)	(2, 7)	(6, 2)	(-1, -18)
(-11, 19)	(0, 7)	(0, 7)	(7, 3)	(-1, -19)
(-9, 19)	(-1, 8)	(0, 9)	**STOP**	(3, -19)
(-7, 17)	(-1, 10)	(2, 9)		(3, -18)
(-5, 19)	(0, 11)	(2, 7)	**START**	(2, -17)
(-3, 19)	(2, 11)	**STOP**	(0, 3)	(2, -12)
(-2, 18)	(3, 10)		(2, 3)	**STOP**
(-2, 15)	(3, 9)	**START**	**STOP**	
(-7, 10)	(5, 9)	(5, 9)		**START**
(-7, -4)	(5, 10)	(5, 8)	**START**	(6, -12)
(-4, -7)	(6, 11)	(6, 7)	(6, 3)	(6, -17)
(-5, -8)	(8, 11)	(8, 7)	(8, 3)	(5, -18)
(-5, -9)	(9, 10)	(8, 9)	**STOP**	(5, -19)
(-2, -9)	(9, 8)	(6, 9)		(9, -19)
(-2, -3)	(8, 7)	(6, 7)	**START**	(9, -18)
(0, -1)	(10, 5)	**STOP**	(9, 0)	(8, -17)
(-1, 0)	(10, 1)		(12, -3)	(8, -12)
(-4, -3)	(8, -1)	**START**	(12, -7)	**STOP**
(-4, -7)	(10, -3)	(3, 6)	(13, -8)	
STOP	(10, -10)	**STOP**	(13, -9)	
	(8, -12)		(10, -9)	
START	(0, -12)	**START**	**STOP**	
(-3, -9)	(-2, -10)	(5, 6)		
(-3, -11)	(-2, -9)	**STOP**		
(-4, -12)	**STOP**			
STOP		**START**		
		(0, -1)		
		(8, -1)		
		STOP		

Name: ____________________

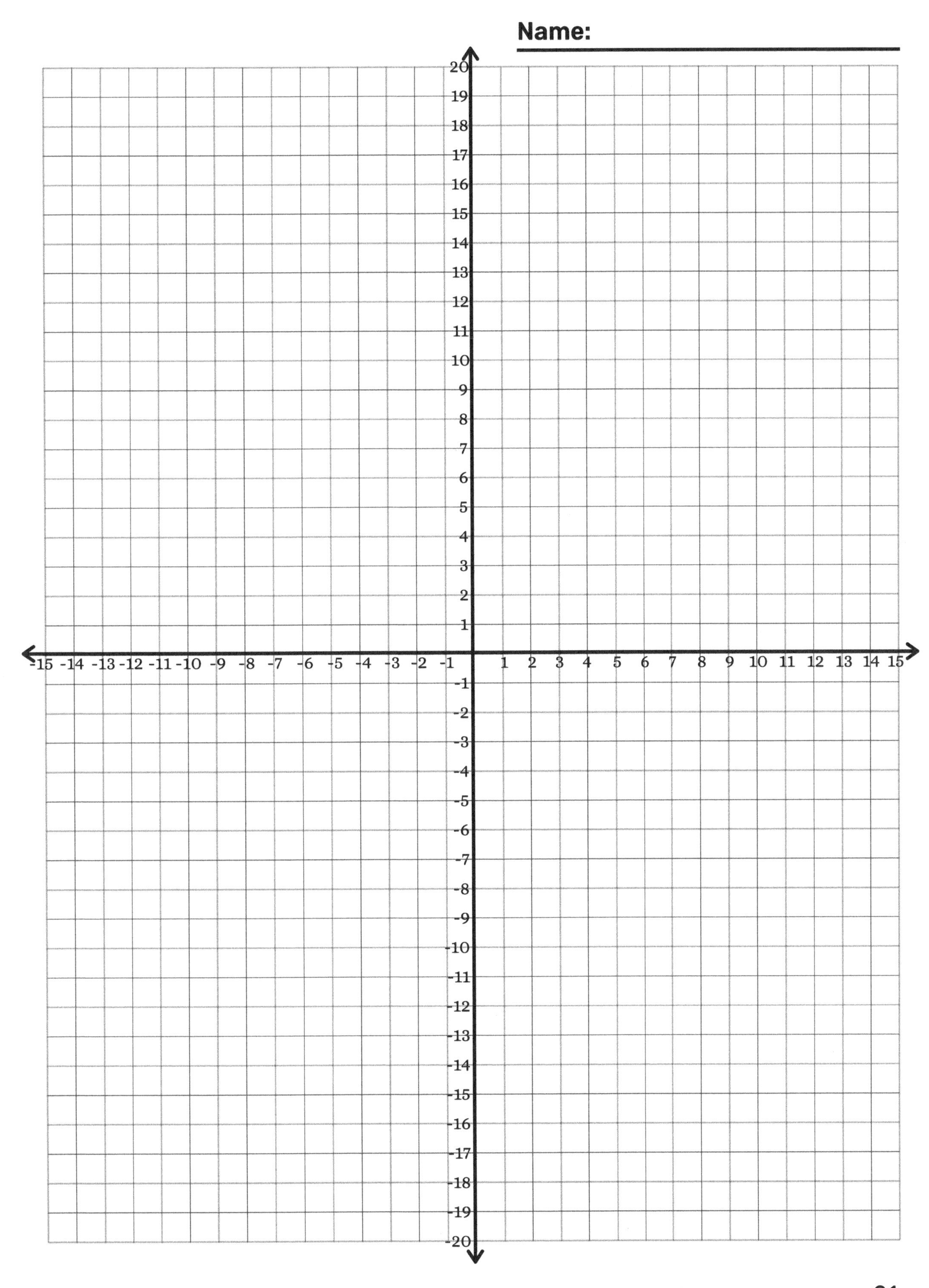

20
19
18
17
16
15
14
13
12
11
10
9
8
7
6
5
4
3
2
1
-15 -14 -13 -12 -11 -10 -9 -8 -7 -6 -5 -4 -3 -2 -1
1 2 3 4 5 6 7 8 9 10 11 12 13 14 15
-1
-2
-3
-4
-5
-6
-7
-8
-9
-10
-11
-12
-13
-14
-15
-16
-17
-18
-19
-20

PRESIDENT'S DAY MYSTERY PICTURE #1 (FIRST QUADRANT)

Plot the ordered pairs, connecting with straight lines as you go. Be sure to stop when you reach **"STOP"** and begin a new series of connected lines at each **"START"**. *Have fun!*

START
(8, 27)
(8, 22)
(1, 22)
(1, 31)
(4, 34)
(26, 34)
(29, 31)
(29, 22)
(22, 22)
(22, 27)
(17, 27)
(16, 28)
(14, 28)
(13, 27)
(8, 27)
STOP

START
(13, 27)
(13, 24)
(12, 23)
(12, 27)
(10, 27)
(10, 23)
(8, 21)
(8, 12)
(3, 7)
(3, 5)
(5, 3)
(25, 3)
(27, 5)
(27, 7)
(22, 12)
(22, 21)
(20, 23)
(20, 27)
(18, 27)
(18, 23)
(17, 24)
(17, 27)
STOP

START
(8, 21)
(22, 21)
STOP

START
(10, 23)
(20, 23)
STOP

START
(12, 16)
(11, 15)
(11, 11)
(14, 8)
(14, 3)
STOP

START
(12, 3)
(13, 2)
(17, 2)
(18, 3)
STOP

Name: ______________________

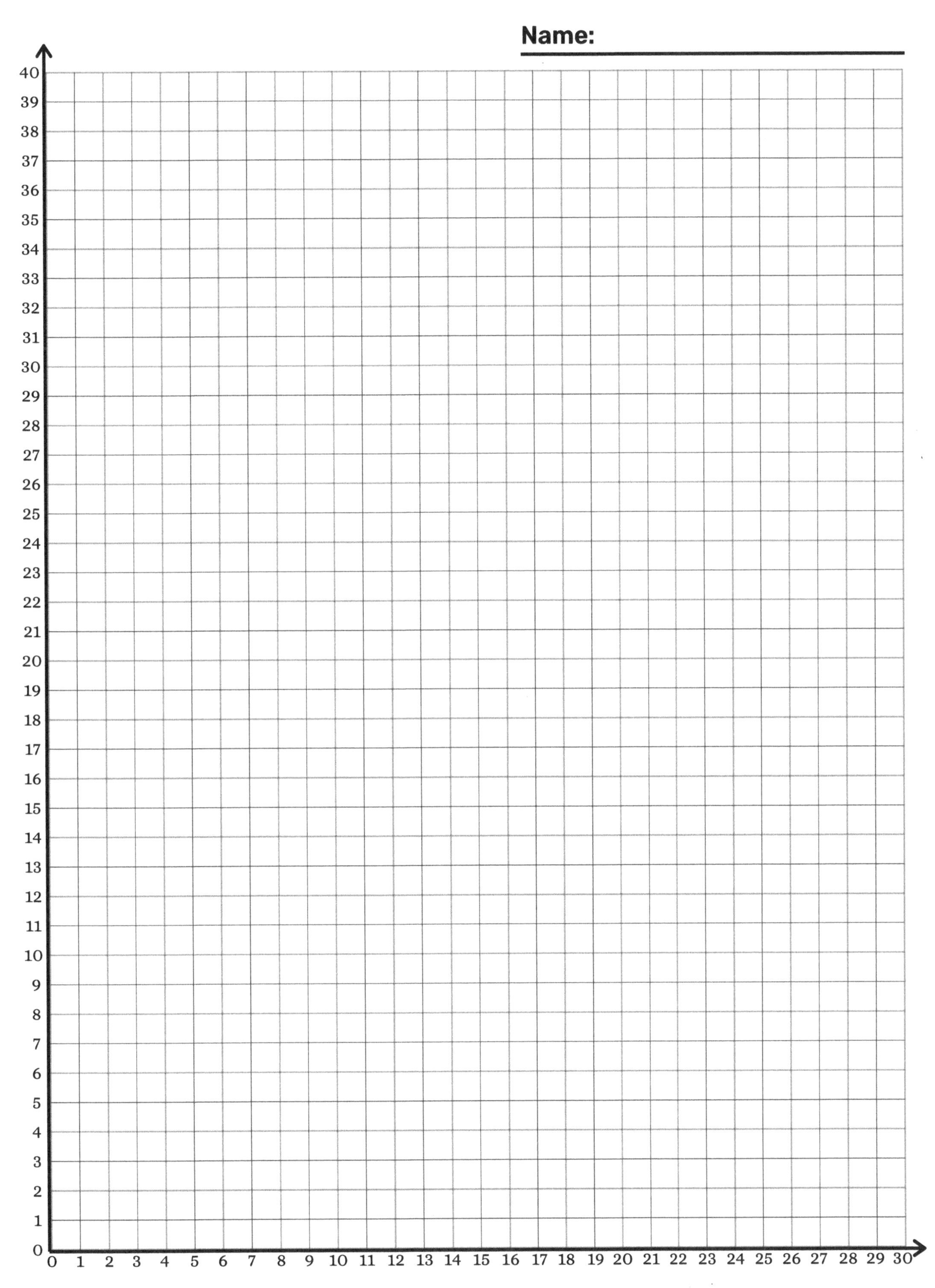

40
39
38
37
36
35
34
33
32
31
30
29
28
27
26
25
24
23
22
21
20
19
18
17
16
15
14
13
12
11
10
9
8
7
6
5
4
3
2
1
0
0 1 2 3 4 5 6 7 8 9 10 11 12 13 14 15 16 17 18 19 20 21 22 23 24 25 26 27 28 29 30

PRESIDENT'S DAY MYSTERY PICTURE #1 (FOUR QUADRANT)

Plot the ordered pairs, connecting with straight lines as you go. Be sure to stop when you reach **"STOP"** and begin a new series of connected lines at each **"START"**. *Have fun!*

START
(-7, 7)
(-7, 2)
(-14, 2)
(-14, 11)
(-11, 14)
(11, 14)
(14, 11)
(14, 2)
(7, 2)
(7, 7)
(2, 7)
(1, 8)
(-1, 8)
(-2, 7)
(-7, 7)
STOP

START
(-2, 7)
(-2, 4)
(-3, 3)
(-3, 7)
(-5, 7)
(-5, 3)
(-7, 1)
(-7, -8)
(-12, -13)
(-12, -15)
(-10, -17)
(10, -17)
(12, -15)
(12, -13)
(7, -8)
(7, 1)
(5, 3)
(5, 7)
(3, 7)
(3, 3)
(2, 4)
(2, 7)
STOP

START
(-7, 1)
(7, 1)
STOP

START
(-5, 3)
(5, 3)
STOP

START
(-3, -4)
(-4, -5)
(-4, -9)
(-1, -12)
(-1, -17)
STOP

START
(-3, -17)
(-2, -18)
(2, -18)
(3, -17)
STOP

Name: ____________________

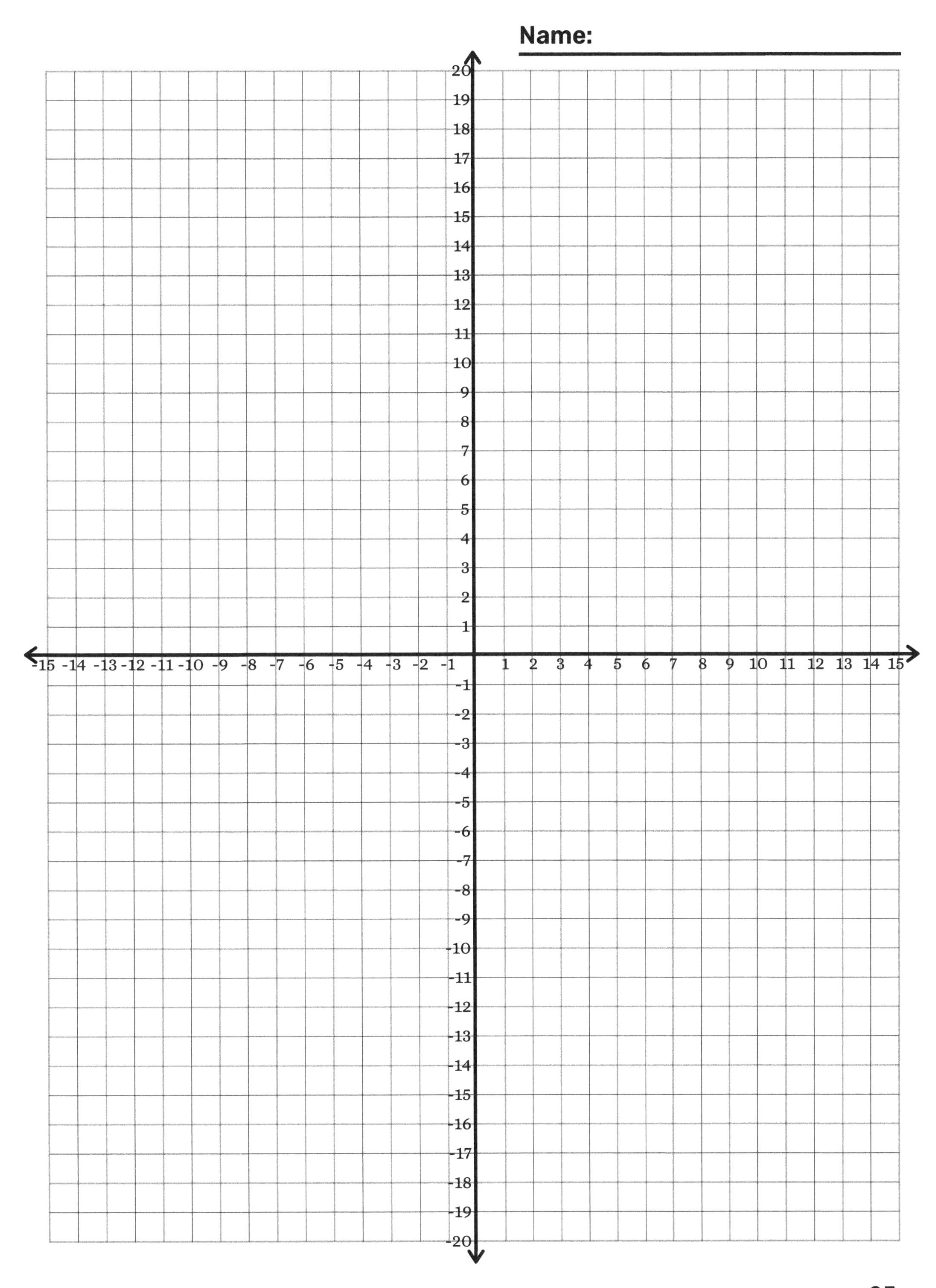

PRESIDENT'S DAY MYSTERY PICTURE #2 (FIRST QUADRANT)

Plot the ordered pairs, connecting with straight lines as you go. Be sure to stop when you reach **"STOP"** and begin a new series of connected lines at each **"START"**. *Have fun!*

<table>
<tr>
<td>**START**
(19, 28)
(16, 25)
(15, 25)
(6, 16)
(6, 15)
(7, 14)
(7, 12)
(1, 6)
(1, 5)
(2, 5)
(3, 6)
(2, 5)
(2, 4)
(3, 4)
(4, 5)
(3, 4)
(3, 3)
(4, 3)
(5, 4)
(4, 3)
(4, 2)
(5, 2)
(6, 3)
(5, 2)
(5, 1)
(6, 1)
(12, 7)
(13, 6)
(16, 6)
(17, 7)
(19, 7)
(26, 14)
(26, 23)
(25, 24)
(25, 26)
(26, 27)
(27, 27)
(28, 26)</td>
<td>(28, 28)
(26, 30)
(26, 32)
(25, 33)
(21, 33)
(19, 31)
(19, 28)
STOP
START
(8, 15)
(7, 14)
(8, 13)
(9, 13)
(10, 14)
(9, 13)
(10, 12)
(11, 12)
(12, 13)
(11, 12)
(12, 11)
(13, 11)
(18, 16)
(18, 15)
(18, 19)
STOP
START
(22, 10)
(24, 10)
(24, 11)
(24, 10)
(26, 10)
(26, 12)
(26, 10)
(28, 12)
(28, 19)
(26, 21)
STOP</td>
<td>**START**
(23, 30)
(24, 30)
(24, 31)
(23, 31)
(23, 30)
STOP
START
(26, 30)
(24, 28)
(25, 28)
(26, 27)
STOP
START
(16, 25)
(16, 23)
(17, 22)
(18, 23)
(19, 22)
(20, 23)
(21, 22)
(22, 23)
(23, 22)
(24, 23)
(25, 22)
(26, 23)
STOP
START
(13, 6)
(13, 4)
(14, 3)
(12, 1)
(13, 1)
(14, 2)
(14, 1)
(15, 1)</td>
<td>(15, 2)
(16, 1)
(17, 1)
(15, 3)
(14, 3)
(15, 3)
(16, 4)
(16, 6)
STOP
START
(18, 7)
(18, 5)
(19, 4)
(17, 2)
(18, 2)
(19, 3)
(19, 2)
(20, 2)
(20, 3)
(21, 2)
(22, 2)
(20, 4)
(19, 4)
(20, 4)
(21, 5)
(21, 9)
STOP
START
(17, 26)
(3, 26)
(3, 38)
(25, 38)
(25, 33)
STOP</td>
<td>**START**
(8, 38)
(8, 33)
(3, 33)
STOP
START
(8, 36)
(25, 36)
STOP
START
(8, 34)
(25, 34)
STOP
START
(3, 32)
(20, 32)
STOP
START
(3, 30)
(19, 30)
STOP
START
(3, 28)
(19, 28)
STOP</td>
<td>**DOTS AT EACH COORDINATE:**
(4, 37)
(5, 37)
(6, 37)
(7, 37)
(4, 36)
(5, 36)
(6, 36)
(7, 36)
(4, 35)
(5, 35)
(6, 36)
(7, 35)
(4, 34)
(5, 34)
(6, 34)
(7, 34)
STOP</td>
</tr>
</table>

Name: ______________________

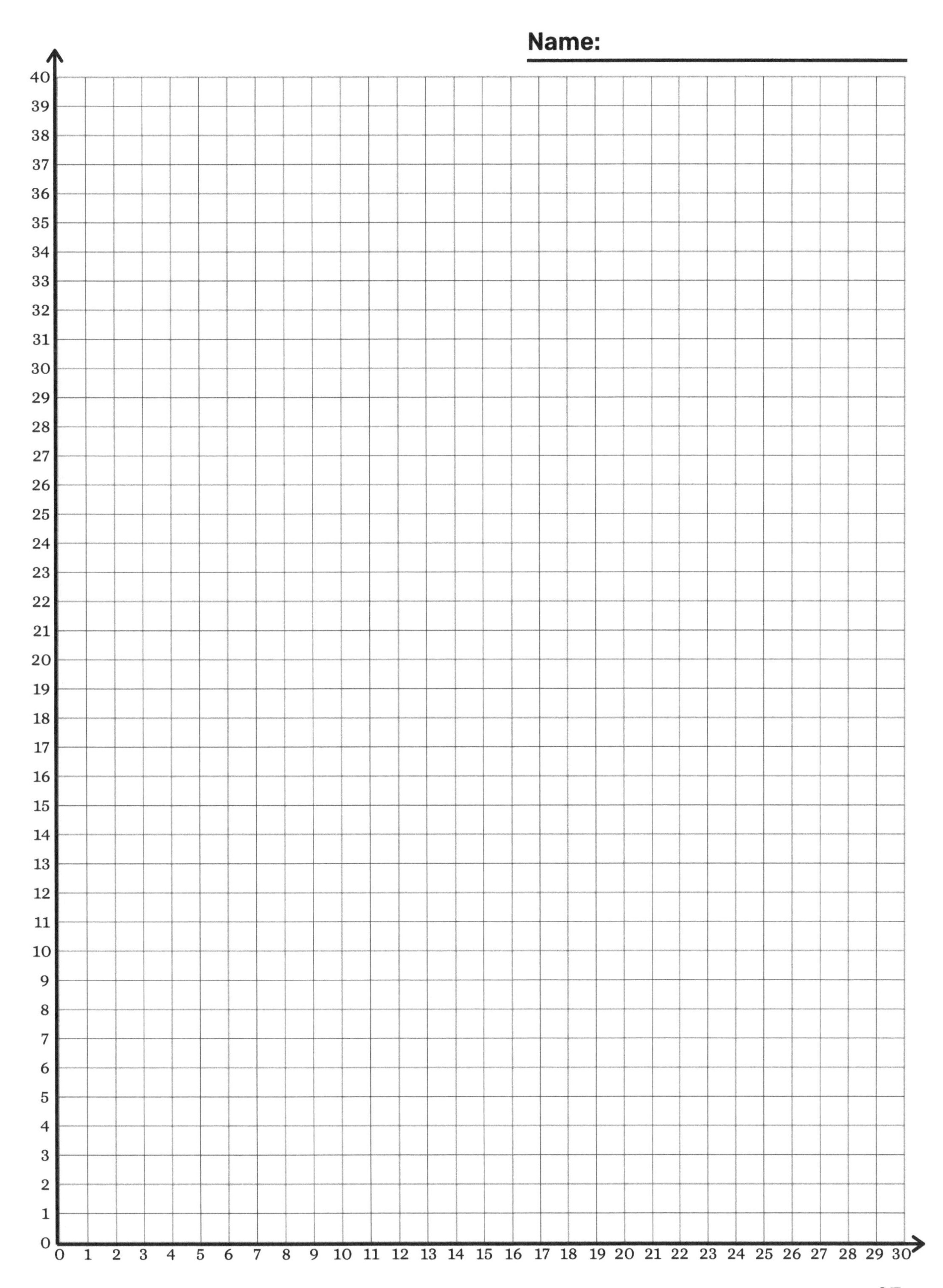

40
39
38
37
36
35
34
33
32
31
30
29
28
27
26
25
24
23
22
21
20
19
18
17
16
15
14
13
12
11
10
9
8
7
6
5
4
3
2
1
0
0 1 2 3 4 5 6 7 8 9 10 11 12 13 14 15 16 17 18 19 20 21 22 23 24 25 26 27 28 29 30

PRESIDENT'S DAY MYSTERY PICTURE #2 (FOUR QUADRANT)

Plot the ordered pairs, connecting with straight lines as you go. Be sure to stop when you reach **"STOP"** and begin a new series of connected lines at each **"START"**. *Have fun!*

<table>
<tr>
<td>**START**
(4, 8)
(1, 5)
(0, 5)
(-9, -4)
(-9, -5)
(-8, -6)
(-8, -8)
(-14, -14)
(-14, -15)
(-13, -15)
(-12, -14)
(-13, -15)
(-13, -16)
(-12, -16)
(-11, -15)
(-12, -16)
(-12, -17)
(-11, -17)
(-10, -16)
(-11, -17)
(-11, -18)
(-10, -18)
(-9, -17)
(-10, -18)
(-10, -19)
(-9, -19)
(-3, -13)
(-2, -14)
(1, -14)
(2, -13)
(4, -13)
(11, -6)
(11, 3)
(10, 4)
(10, 6)
(11, 7)
(12, 7)
(13, 6)</td>
<td>(13, 8)
(11, 10)
(11, 12)
(10, 13)
(6, 13)
(4, 11)
(4, 8)
STOP
START
(-7, -5)
(-8, -6)
(-7, -7)
(-6, -7)
(-5, -6)
(-6, -7)
(-5, -8)
(-4, -8)
(-3, -7)
(-4, -8)
(-3, -9)
(-2, -9)
(3, -4)
(3, -5)
(3, -1)
STOP
START
(7, -10)
(9, -10)
(9, -9)
(9, -10)
(11, -10)
(11, -8)
(11, -10)
(13, -8)
(13, -1)
(11, 1)
STOP</td>
<td>**START**
(8, 10)
(9, 10)
(9, 11)
(8, 11)
(8, 10)
STOP
START
(11, 10)
(9, 8)
(10, 8)
(11, 7)
STOP
START
(1, 5)
(1, 3)
(2, 2)
(3, 3)
(4, 2)
(5, 3)
(6, 2)
(7, 3)
(8, 2)
(9, 3)
(10, 2)
(11, 3)
STOP</td>
<td>**START**
(-2, -14)
(-2, -16)
(-1, -17)
(-3, -19)
(-2, -19)
(-1, -18)
(-1, -19)
(0, -19)
(0, -18)
(1, -19)
(2, -19)
(0, -17)
(-1, -17)
(0, -17)
(1, -16)
(1, -14)
STOP
START
(3, -13)
(3, -15)
(4, -16)
(2, -18)
(3, -18)
(4, -17)
(4, -18)
(5, -18)
(5, -17)
(6, -18)
(7, -18)
(5, -16)
(4, -16)
(5, -16)
(6, -15)
(6, -11)
STOP</td>
<td>**START**
(2, 6)
(-12, 6)
(-12, 18)
(10, 18)
(10, 13)
STOP
START
(-7, 18)
(-7, 13)
(-12, 13)
STOP
START
(-7, 16)
(10, 16)
STOP
START
(-7, 14)
(10, 14)
STOP
START
(-12, 12)
(5, 12)
STOP
START
(-12, 10)
(4, 10)
STOP
START
(-12, 8)
(4, 8)
STOP</td>
<td>**DOTS AT EACH COORDINATE:**
(-11, 17)
(-10, 17)
(-9, 17)
(-8, 17)
(-11, 16)
(-10, 16)
(-9, 16)
(-8, 16)
(-11, 15)
(-10, 15)
(-9, 15)
(-8, 15)
(-11, 14)
(-10, 14)
(-9, 14)
(-8, 14)
STOP</td>
</tr>
</table>

Name: ______________________

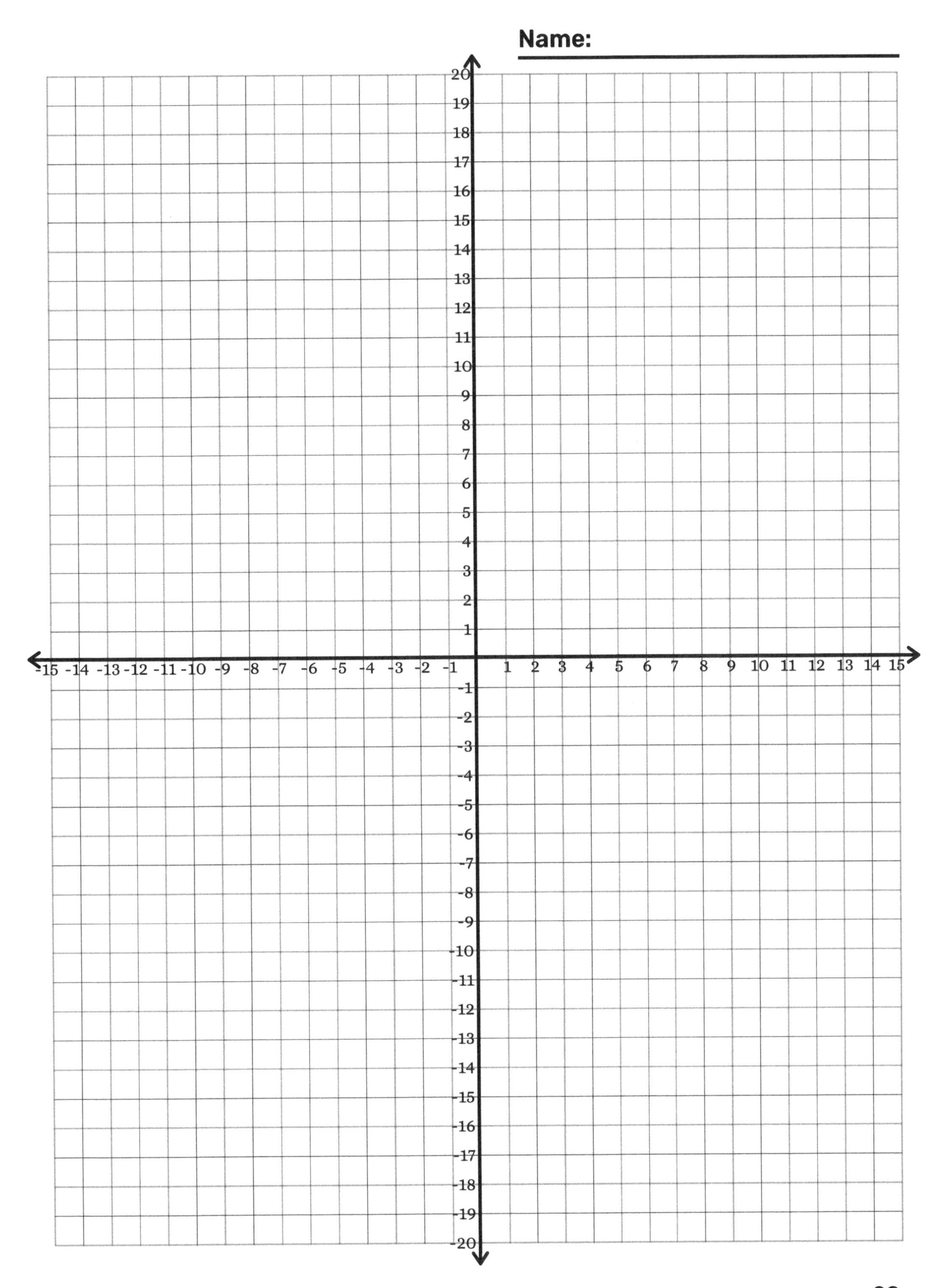

20
19
18
17
16
15
14
13
12
11
10
9
8
7
6
5
4
3
2
1
-15 -14 -13 -12 -11 -10 -9 -8 -7 -6 -5 -4 -3 -2 -1
1 2 3 4 5 6 7 8 9 10 11 12 13 14 15
-1
-2
-3
-4
-5
-6
-7
-8
-9
-10
-11
-12
-13
-14
-15
-16
-17
-18
-19
-20

ST. PATRICK'S DAY MYSTERY PICTURE #1 (FIRST QUADRANT)

Plot the ordered pairs, connecting with straight lines as you go. Be sure to stop when you reach **"STOP"** and begin a new series of connected lines at each **"START"**. *Have fun!*

START
(6, 21)
(4, 19)
(4, 7)
(7, 4)
(9, 4)
(11, 2)
(13, 2)
(14, 1)
(17, 1)
(18, 2)
(20, 2)
(22, 4)
(24, 4)
(27, 7)
(27, 19)
(25, 21)
STOP

START
(6, 21)
(1, 21)
(1, 24)
(7, 24)
(7, 39)
(24, 39)
(24, 24)
(30, 24)
(30, 21)
(6, 21)
STOP

START
(4, 19)
(3, 20)
(3, 15)
(4, 16)
(6, 14)
(8, 14)
(9, 13)
(11, 13)
(12, 12)
(19, 12)
(20, 13)
(22, 13)
(23, 14)
(25, 14)
(27, 16)
(28, 15)
(28, 20)
(27, 19)
STOP

START
(7, 24)
(12, 24)
(12, 23)
(19, 23)
(19, 24)
(24, 24)
STOP

START
(15, 30)
(16, 30)
(16, 33)
(17, 32)
(18, 32)
(19, 33)
(19, 34)
(18, 35)
(17, 35)
(16, 34)
(17, 35)
(17, 36)
(16, 37)
(15, 37)
(14, 36)
(14, 35)
(15, 34)
(14, 35)
(13, 35)
(12, 34)
(12, 33)
(13, 32)
(14, 32)
(15, 33)
(15, 30)
STOP

START
(12, 24)
(12, 29)
(19, 29)
(19, 24)
STOP

START
(7, 28)
(12, 28)
STOP

START
(19, 28)
(24, 28)
STOP

START
(14, 27)
(17, 27)
(17, 25)
(14, 25)
(14, 27)
STOP

START
(12, 20)
(14, 20)
(14, 18)
(12, 18)
(12, 20)
STOP

START
(17, 20)
(19, 20)
(19, 18)
(17, 18)
(17, 20)
STOP

START
(14, 16)
(15, 15)
(16, 15)
(17, 16)
STOP

START
(11, 15)
(10, 15)
(10, 16)
(11, 16)
(11, 15)
(13, 13)
(18, 13)
(20, 15)
(20, 16)
(21, 16)
(21, 15)
(20, 15)
STOP

PLOT A DOT AT EACH COORDINATE:
(13, 19)
(18, 19)

Name: ____________________

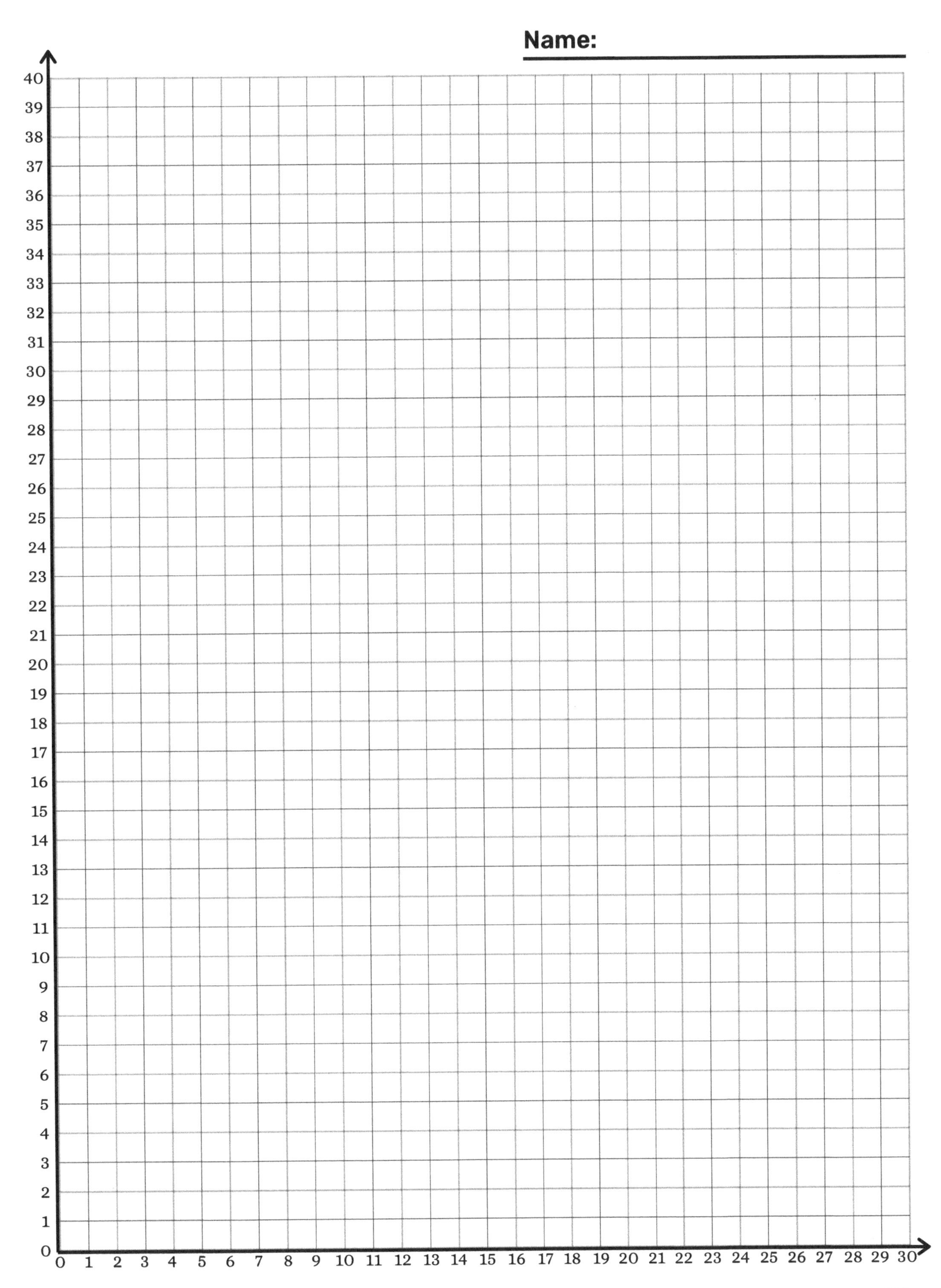

40
39
38
37
36
35
34
33
32
31
30
29
28
27
26
25
24
23
22
21
20
19
18
17
16
15
14
13
12
11
10
9
8
7
6
5
4
3
2
1
0
0 1 2 3 4 5 6 7 8 9 10 11 12 13 14 15 16 17 18 19 20 21 22 23 24 25 26 27 28 29 30

ST. PATRICK'S DAY MYSTERY PICTURE #1 (FOUR QUADRANT)

Plot the ordered pairs, connecting with straight lines as you go. Be sure to stop when you reach **"STOP"** and begin a new series of connected lines at each **"START"**. *Have fun!*

START
(-9, 1)
(-14, 1)
(-14, 4)
(-8, 4)
(-8, 19)
(9, 19)
(9, 4)
(15, 4)
(15, 1)
(-9, 1)
STOP

START
(10, 1)
(12, -1)
(12, -13)
(9, -16)
(7, -16)
(5, -18)
(3, -18)
(2, -19)
(-1, -19)
(-2, -18)
(-4, -18)
(-6, -16)
(-8, -16)
(-11, -13)
(-11, -1)
(-9, 1)
STOP

START
(-11, -1)
(-12, 0)
(-12, -5)
(-11, -4)
(-9, -6)
(-7, -6)
(-6, -7)
(-4, -7)
(-3, -8)
(4, -8)
(5, -7)
(7, -7)
(8, -6)
(10, -6)
(12, -4)
(12, -5)
(13, 0)
(12, -1)
STOP

START
(-8, 4)
(-3, 4)
(-3, 3)
(4, 3)
(4, 4)
(9, 4)
STOP

START
(0, 10)
(1, 10)
(1, 13)
(2, 12)
(3, 12)
(4, 13)
(4, 14)
(3, 15)
(2, 15)
(1, 14)
(2, 15)
(2, 16)
(1, 17)
(0, 17)
(-1, 16)
(-1, 15)
(0, 14)
(-1, 15)
(-2, 15)
(-3, 14)
(-3, 13)
(-2, 12)
(-1, 12)
(0, 13)
(0, 10)
STOP

START
(-3, 4)
(-3, 9)
(4, 9)
(4, 4)
STOP

START
(-8, 8)
(-3, 8)
STOP

START
(4, 8)
(9, 8)
STOP

START
(-1, 7)
(2, 7)
(2, 5)
(-1, 5)
(-1, 7)
STOP

START
(-3, 0)
(-1, 0)
(-1, -2)
(-3, -2)
(-3, 0)
STOP

START
(2, 0)
(4, 0)
(4, -2)
(2, -2)
(2, 0)
STOP

START
(-1, -4)
(0, -5)
(1, -5)
(2, 4)
STOP

START
(-4, -5)
(-5, -5)
(-5, -4)
(-4, -4)
(-4, -5)
(-2, -7)
(3, -7)
(5, -5)
(5, -4)
(6, -4)
(6, -5)
(5, -5)
STOP

PLOT A DOT AT EACH COORDINATE:
(-2, -1)
(3, -1)

Name: ______________________

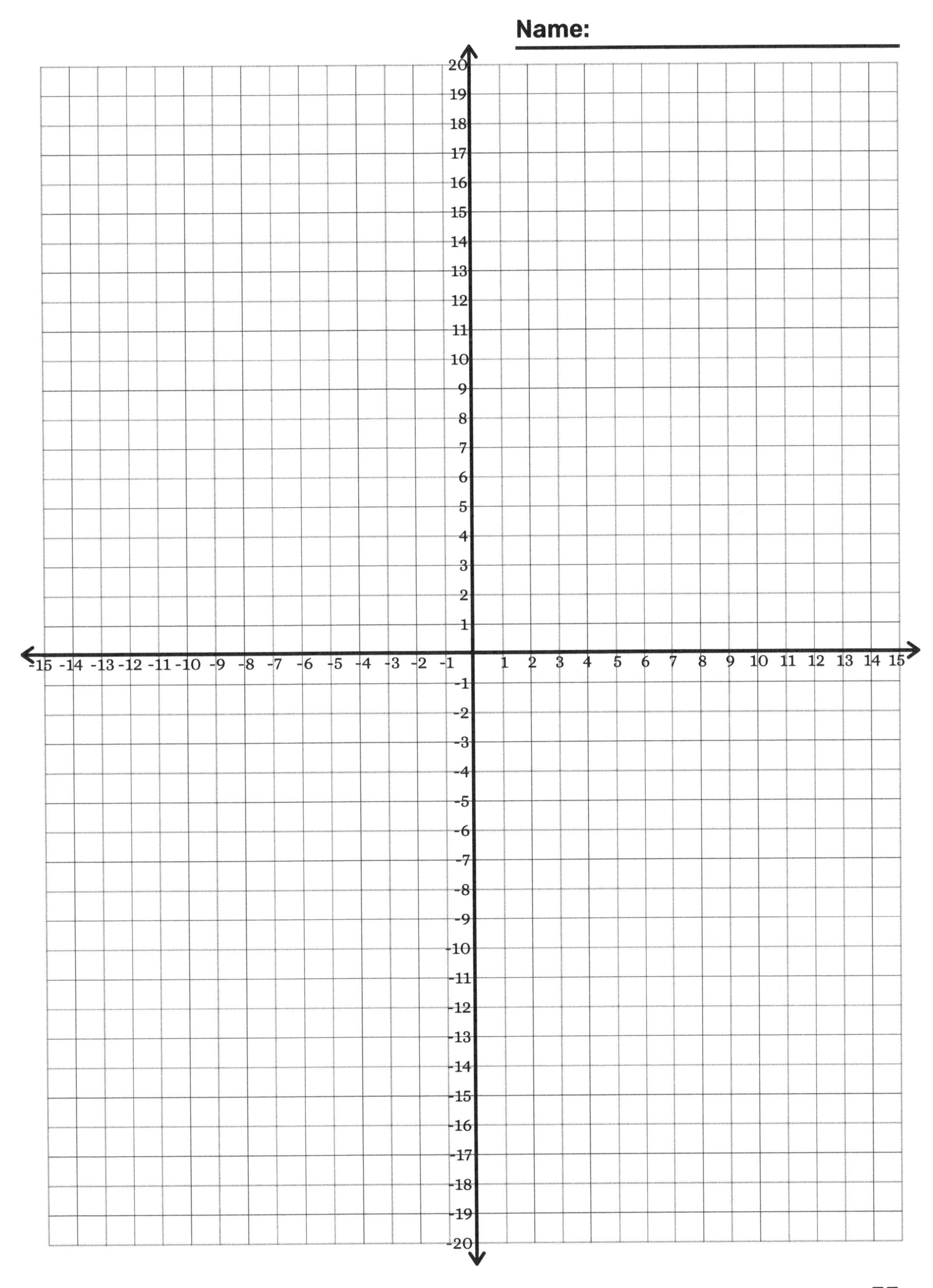

20
19
18
17
16
15
14
13
12
11
10
9
8
7
6
5
4
3
2
1
-15 -14 -13 -12 -11 -10 -9 -8 -7 -6 -5 -4 -3 -2 -1
1 2 3 4 5 6 7 8 9 10 11 12 13 14 15
-1
-2
-3
-4
-5
-6
-7
-8
-9
-10
-11
-12
-13
-14
-15
-16
-17
-18
-19
-20

ST. PATRICK'S DAY MYSTERY PICTURE #2 (FIRST QUADRANT)

Plot the ordered pairs, connecting with straight lines as you go. Be sure to stop when you reach **"STOP"** and begin a new series of connected lines at each **"START"**. *Have fun!*

START (1, 17) (1, 16) (2, 15) (1, 14) (1, 7) (5, 3) (17, 3) (21, 7) (21, 14) (20, 15) (21, 16) (21, 17) (20, 18) (19, 18) (18, 19) (17, 19) (16, 20) (6, 20) (5, 19) (4, 19) (3, 18) (2, 18) (1, 17) **STOP**	**START** (1, 17) (21, 17) **STOP** **START** (2, 15) (20, 15) **STOP** **START** (4, 19) (25, 40) **STOP** **START** (7, 20) (27, 40) **STOP** **START** (9, 20) (29, 40) **STOP** **START** (11, 20) (30, 39) **STOP**	**START** (13, 20) (30, 37) **STOP** **START** (15, 20) (30, 35) **STOP** **START** (17, 20) (30, 33) **STOP** **START** (18, 19) (30, 31) **STOP**

Name: ______________________

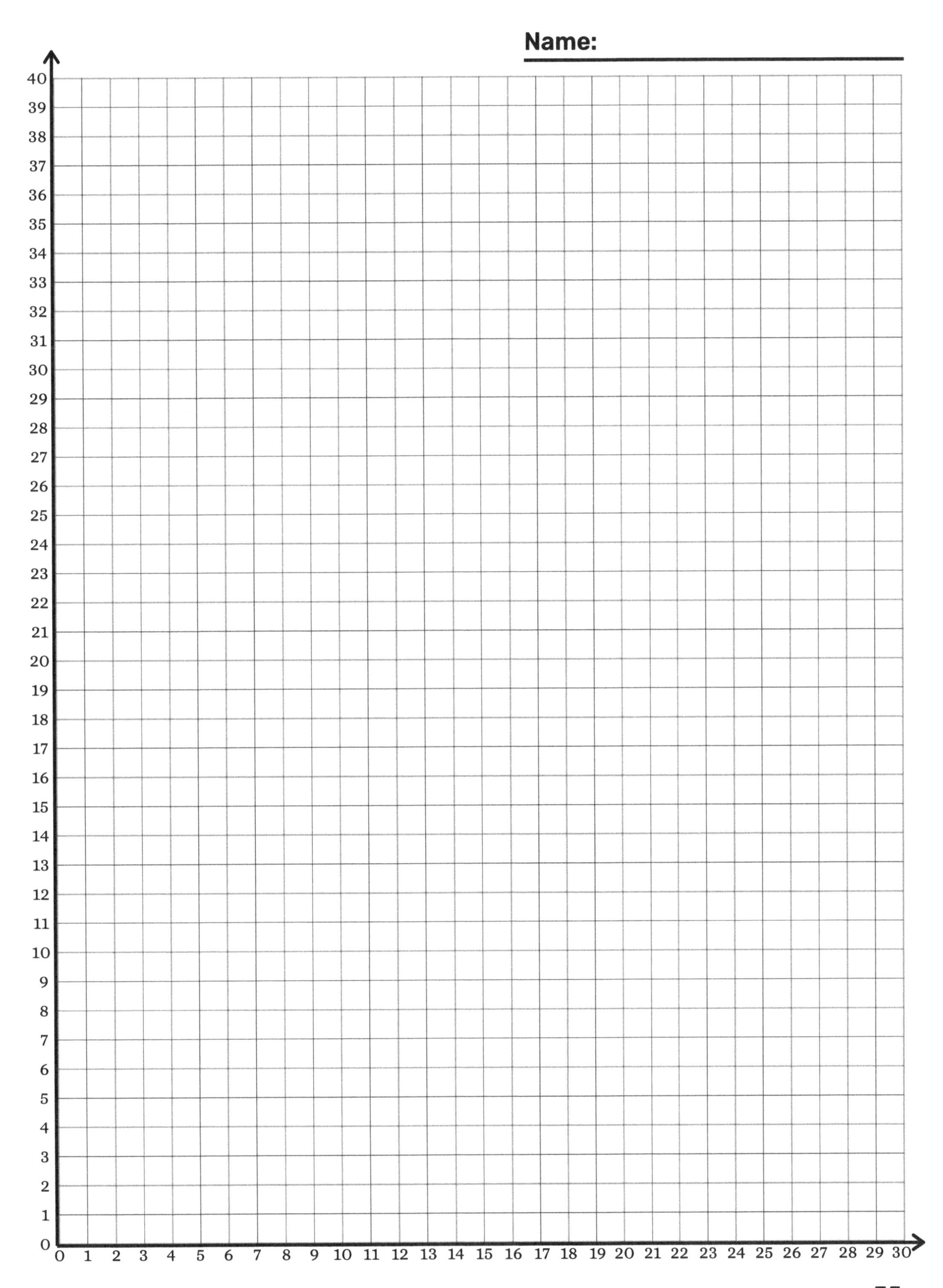
40
39
38
37
36
35
34
33
32
31
30
29
28
27
26
25
24
23
22
21
20
19
18
17
16
15
14
13
12
11
10
9
8
7
6
5
4
3
2
1
0
0 1 2 3 4 5 6 7 8 9 10 11 12 13 14 15 16 17 18 19 20 21 22 23 24 25 26 27 28 29 30

ST. PATRICK'S DAY MYSTERY PICTURE #2 (FOUR QUADRANT)

Plot the ordered pairs, connecting with straight lines as you go. Be sure to stop when you reach **"STOP"** and begin a new series of connected lines at each **"START"**. *Have fun!*

START (-14, -3) (-14, -4) (-13, -5) (-14, -6) (-14, -13) (-10, -17) (2, -17) (6, -13) (6, -6) (5, -5) (6, -4) (6, -3) (5, -2) (4, -2) (3, -1) (2, -1) (1, 0) (-9, 0) (-10, -1) (-11, -1) (-12, -2) (-13, -2) (-14, -3) **STOP**	**START** (-14, -3) (6, -3) **STOP** **START** (-13, -5) (5, -5) **STOP** **START** (-11, -1) (10, 20) **STOP** **START** (-8, 0) (12, 20) **STOP** **START** (-6, 0) (14, 20) **STOP** **START** (-4, 0) (15, 19) **STOP**	**START** (-2, 0) (15, 17) **STOP** **START** (0, 0) (15, 15) **STOP** **START** (2, 0) (15, 13) **STOP** **START** (3, -1) (15, 11) **STOP**

Name: ______________________

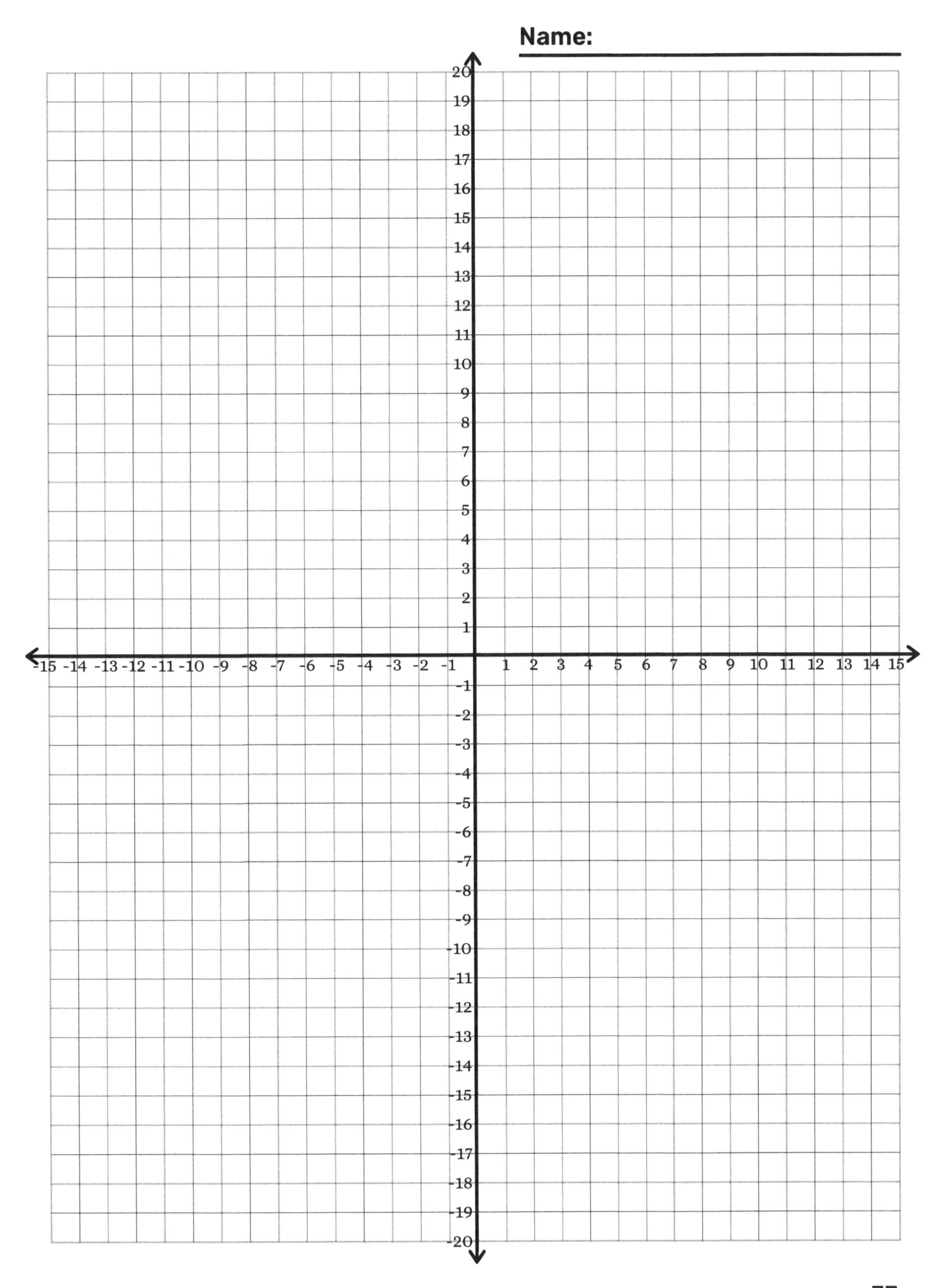

20 19 18 17 16 15 14 13 12 11 10 9 8 7 6 5 4 3 2 1
-15 -14 -13 -12 -11 -10 -9 -8 -7 -6 -5 -4 -3 -2 -1
1 2 3 4 5 6 7 8 9 10 11 12 13 14 15
-1 -2 -3 -4 -5 -6 -7 -8 -9 -10 -11 -12 -13 -14 -15 -16 -17 -18 -19 -20

SPRING MYSTERY PICTURE #1 (FIRST QUADRANT)

Plot the ordered pairs, connecting with straight lines as you go. Be sure to stop when you reach **"STOP"** and begin a new series of connected lines at each **"START"**. *Have fun!*

START
(0, 13)
(0, 10)
(25, 10)
(25, 9)
(26, 9)
(25, 10)
(27, 10)
(27, 9)
(28, 9)
(28, 10)
(27, 10)
(28, 11)
(27, 12)
(25, 12)
(25, 13)
(24, 13)
(25, 12)
(1, 12)
(0, 13)
STOP

START
(5, 22)
(10, 17)
(17, 17)
(21, 21)
(21, 28)
(18, 31)
(14, 31)
(11, 28)
(11, 25)
(8, 22)
(5, 22)
STOP

START
(21, 28)
(23, 28)
(21, 26)
(23, 26)
(21, 24)
STOP

START
(12, 22)
(12, 19)
(14, 19)
(17, 22)
STOP

START
(18, 28)
(17, 28)
(17, 27)
(18, 27)
(18, 29)
(16, 29)
(16, 27)
(17, 27)
STOP

START
(19, 10)
(20, 9)
(19, 9)
(19, 8)
(20, 8)
(20, 9)
(21, 8)
(20, 8)
(20, 7)
(21, 7)
(21, 8)
(22, 7)
(22, 8)
(23, 8)
(23, 9)
(22, 8)
(22, 9)
(21, 10)
STOP

START
(24, 29)
(24, 27)
(25, 27)
(25, 28)
(24, 28)
STOP

START
(25, 33)
(25, 31)
(26, 31)
(26, 32)
(25, 32)
STOP

START
(26, 35)
(27, 35)
(27, 34)
(26, 34)
(26, 36)
(28, 36)
(28, 34)
(29, 34)
(29, 35)
(28, 35)
STOP

START
(23, 39)
(23, 37)
(24, 37)
(24, 38)
(23, 38)
STOP

START
(13, 17)
(13, 11)
(13, 12)
(12, 11)
(13, 12)
(14, 11)
STOP

START
(16, 17)
(16, 11)
(16, 12)
(15, 11)
(16, 12)
(17, 11)
STOP

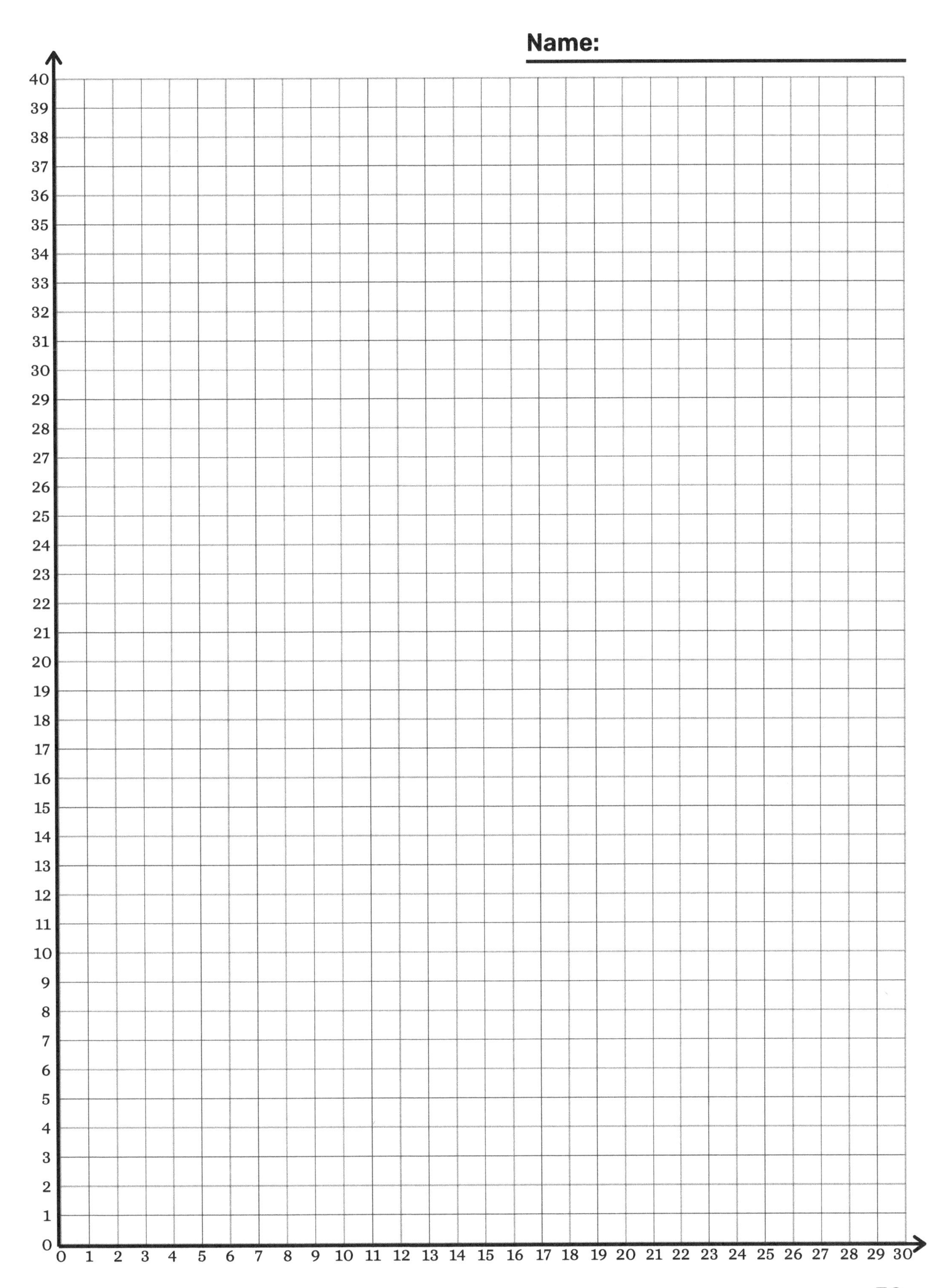
Name:
40
39
38
37
36
35
34
33
32
31
30
29
28
27
26
25
24
23
22
21
20
19
18
17
16
15
14
13
12
11
10
9
8
7
6
5
4
3
2
1
0
0 1 2 3 4 5 6 7 8 9 10 11 12 13 14 15 16 17 18 19 20 21 22 23 24 25 26 27 28 29 30

SPRING MYSTERY PICTURE #1 (FOUR QUADRANT)

Plot the ordered pairs, connecting with straight lines as you go. Be sure to stop when you reach **"STOP"** and begin a new series of connected lines at each **"START"**. *Have fun!*

START
(-15, -7)
(-15, -10)
(10, -10)
(10, -11)
(11, -11)
(10, -10)
(12, -10)
(12, -11)
(13, -11)
(13, -10)
(12, -10)
(13, -9)
(12, -8)
(10, -8)
(10, -7)
(9, -7)
(10, -8)
(-14, -8)
(-15, -7)
STOP

START
(-10, 2)
(-5, -3)
(2, -3)
(6, 1)
(6, 8)
(3, 11)
(-1, 11)
(-4, 8)
(-4, 5)
(-7, 2)
(-10, 2)
STOP

START
(6, 8)
(8, 8)
(6, 6)
(8, 6)
(6, 4)
STOP

START
(-3, 2)
(-3, -1)
(-1, -1)
(2, 2)
STOP

START
(3, 8)
(2, 8)
(2, 7)
(3, 7)
(3, 9)
(1, 9)
(1, 7)
(2, 7)
STOP

START
(4, -10)
(5, -11)
(4, -11)
(4, -12)
(5, -12)
(5, -11)
(6, -12)
(5, -12)
(5, -13)
(6, -13)
(6, -12)
(7, -13)
(7, -12)
(8, -12)
(8, -11)
(7, -12)
(7, -11)
(6, -10)
STOP

START
(9, 9)
(9, 7)
(10, 7)
(10, 8)
(9, 8)
STOP

START
(10, 13)
(10, 11)
(11, 11)
(11, 12)
(10, 12)
STOP

START
(11, 15)
(12, 15)
(12, 14)
(11, 14)
(11, 16)
(13, 16)
(13, 14)
(14, 14)
(14, 15)
(13, 15)
STOP

START
(8, 19)
(8, 17)
(9, 17)
(9, 18)
(8, 18)
STOP

START
(-2, -3)
(-2, -9)
(-2, -8)
(-3, -9)
(-2, -8)
(-1, -9)
STOP

START
(1, -3)
(1, -9)
(1, -8)
(0, -9)
(1, -8)
(2, -9)
STOP

Name: ______________________________

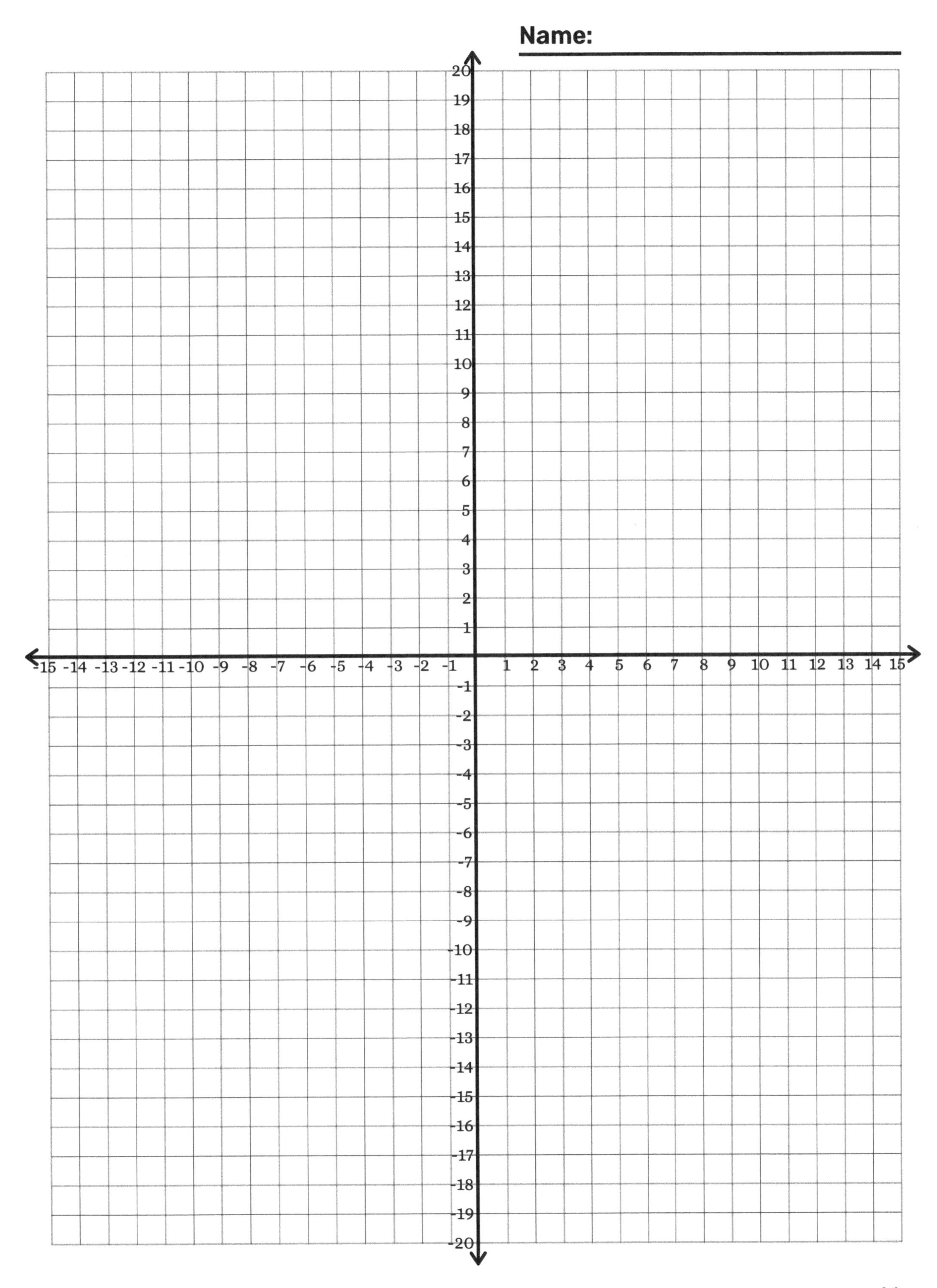

20
19
18
17
16
15
14
13
12
11
10
9
8
7
6
5
4
3
2
1
-15 -14 -13 -12 -11 -10 -9 -8 -7 -6 -5 -4 -3 -2 -1
1 2 3 4 5 6 7 8 9 10 11 12 13 14 15
-1
-2
-3
-4
-5
-6
-7
-8
-9
-10
-11
-12
-13
-14
-15
-16
-17
-18
-19
-20

SPRING MYSTERY PICTURE #2 (FIRST QUADRANT)

Plot the ordered pairs, connecting with straight lines as you go. Be sure to stop when you reach **"STOP"** and begin a new series of connected lines at each **"START"**. *Have fun!*

START
(15, 18)
(15, 7)
(11, 11)
(10, 10)
(15, 5)
(15, 0)
(16, 0)
(16, 5)
(21, 10)
(20, 11)
(16, 7)
(16, 18)
STOP

START
(20, 11)
(19, 12)
(19, 15)
(24, 20)
(29, 20)
(29, 13)
(25, 9)
(22, 9)
(21, 10)
STOP

START
(11, 11)
(12, 12)
(12, 15)
(8, 19)
(1, 19)
(1, 14)
(6, 9)
(9, 9)
(10, 10)
STOP

START
(19, 21)
(19, 20)
(22, 20)
(24, 22)
(24, 25)
(23, 25)
(24, 25)
(26, 27)
(26, 30)
(24, 32)
(23, 32)
(24, 32)
(24, 35)
(22, 37)
(19, 37)
(19, 36)
(19, 37)
(17, 39)
(14, 39)
(12, 37)
(12, 36)
(12, 37)
(9, 37)
(7, 35)
(7, 32)
(8, 32)
(7, 32)
(5, 30)
(5, 27)
(7, 25)
(8, 25)
(7, 25)
(7, 22)
(9, 20)
(12, 20)
(12, 21)
(12, 20)
(14, 18)
(17, 18)
(19, 20)
STOP

START
(18, 23)
(21, 26)
(21, 31)
(18, 34)
(13, 34)
(10, 31)
(10, 26)
(13, 23)
(18, 23)
STOP

START
(12, 29)
(12, 31)
(14, 31)
(14, 29)
(12, 29)
(11, 30)
(11, 32)
(12, 33)
(14, 33)
(15, 32)
(15, 30)
(14, 29)
STOP

START
(19, 29)
(19, 31)
(17, 31)
(17, 29)
(19, 29)
(20, 30)
(20, 32)
(19, 33)
(17, 33)
(16, 32)
(16, 30)
(17, 29)
STOP

START
(12, 26)
(12, 27)
(11, 27)
(11, 26)
(12, 26)
(14, 24)
(17, 24)
(19, 26)
(19, 27)
(20, 27)
(20, 26)
(19, 26)
(18, 25)
(13, 25)
STOP

START
(21, 11)
(26, 16)
STOP

START
(5, 16)
(10, 11)
STOP

Name: ______________________

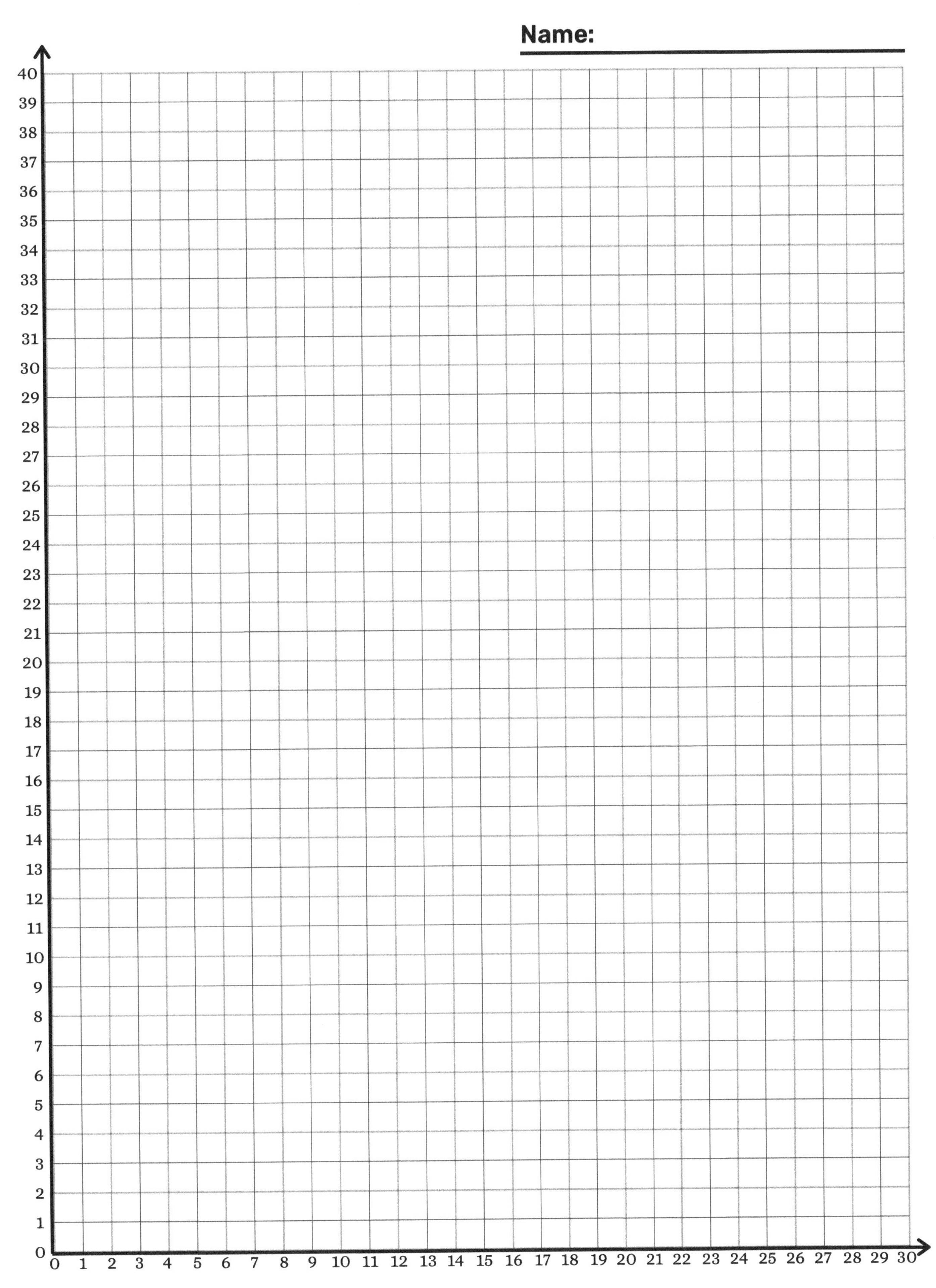

40
39
38
37
36
35
34
33
32
31
30
29
28
27
26
25
24
23
22
21
20
19
18
17
16
15
14
13
12
11
10
9
8
7
6
5
4
3
2
1
0
0 1 2 3 4 5 6 7 8 9 10 11 12 13 14 15 16 17 18 19 20 21 22 23 24 25 26 27 28 29 30

SPRING MYSTERY PICTURE #2 (FOUR QUADRANT)

Plot the ordered pairs, connecting with straight lines as you go. Be sure to stop when you reach **"STOP"** and begin a new series of connected lines at each **"START"**. *Have fun!*

START
(0, -2)
(0, -13)
(-4, -9)
(-5, -10)
(0, -15)
(0, -20)
(1, -20)
(1, -15)
(6, -10)
(5, -9)
(1, -13)
(1, -2)
STOP

START
(5, -9)
(4, -8)
(4, -5)
(9, 0)
(14, 0)
(14, -7)
(10, -11)
(7, -11)
(6, -10)
STOP

START
(-4, -9)
(-3, -8)
(-3, -5)
(-7, -1)
(-14, -1)
(-14, -6)
(-9, -11)
(-6, -11)
(-5, -10)
STOP

START
(4, 1)
(4, 0)
(7, 0)
(9, 2)
(9, 5)
(8, 5)
(9, 5)
(11, 7)
(11, 10)
(9, 12)
(8, 12)
(9, 12)
(9, 15)
(7, 17)
(4, 17)
(4, 16)
(4, 17)
(2, 19)
(-1, 19)
(-3, 17)
(-3, 16)
(-3, 17)
(-6, 17)
(-8, 15)
(-8, 12)
(-7, 12)
(-8, 12)
(-10, 10)
(-10, 7)
(-8, 5)
(-7, 5)
(-8, 5)
(-8, 2)
(-6, 0)
(-3, 0)
(-3, 1)
(-3, 0)
(-1, -2)
(2, -2)
(4, 0)
STOP

START
(3, 3)
(6, 6)
(6, 11)
(3, 14)
(-2, 14)
(-5, 11)
(-5, 6)
(-2, 3)
(3, 3)
STOP

START
(-3, 9)
(-3, 11)
(-1, 11)
(-1, 9)
(-3, 9)
(-4, 10)
(-4, 12)
(-3, 13)
(-1, 13)
(0, 12)
(0, 10)
(-1, 9)
STOP

START
(4, 9)
(4, 11)
(2, 11)
(2, 9)
(4, 9)
(5, 10)
(5, 12)
(4, 13)
(2, 13)
(1, 12)
(1, 10)
(2, 9)
STOP

START
(-3, 6)
(-3, 7)
(-4, 7)
(-4, 6)
(-3, 6)
(-1, 4)
(2, 4)
(4, 6)
(4, 7)
(5, 7)
(5, 6)
(4, 6)
(3, 5)
(-2, 5)
STOP

START
(6, -9)
(11, -4)
STOP

START
(-10, -4)
(-5, -9)
STOP

Name: ______________________

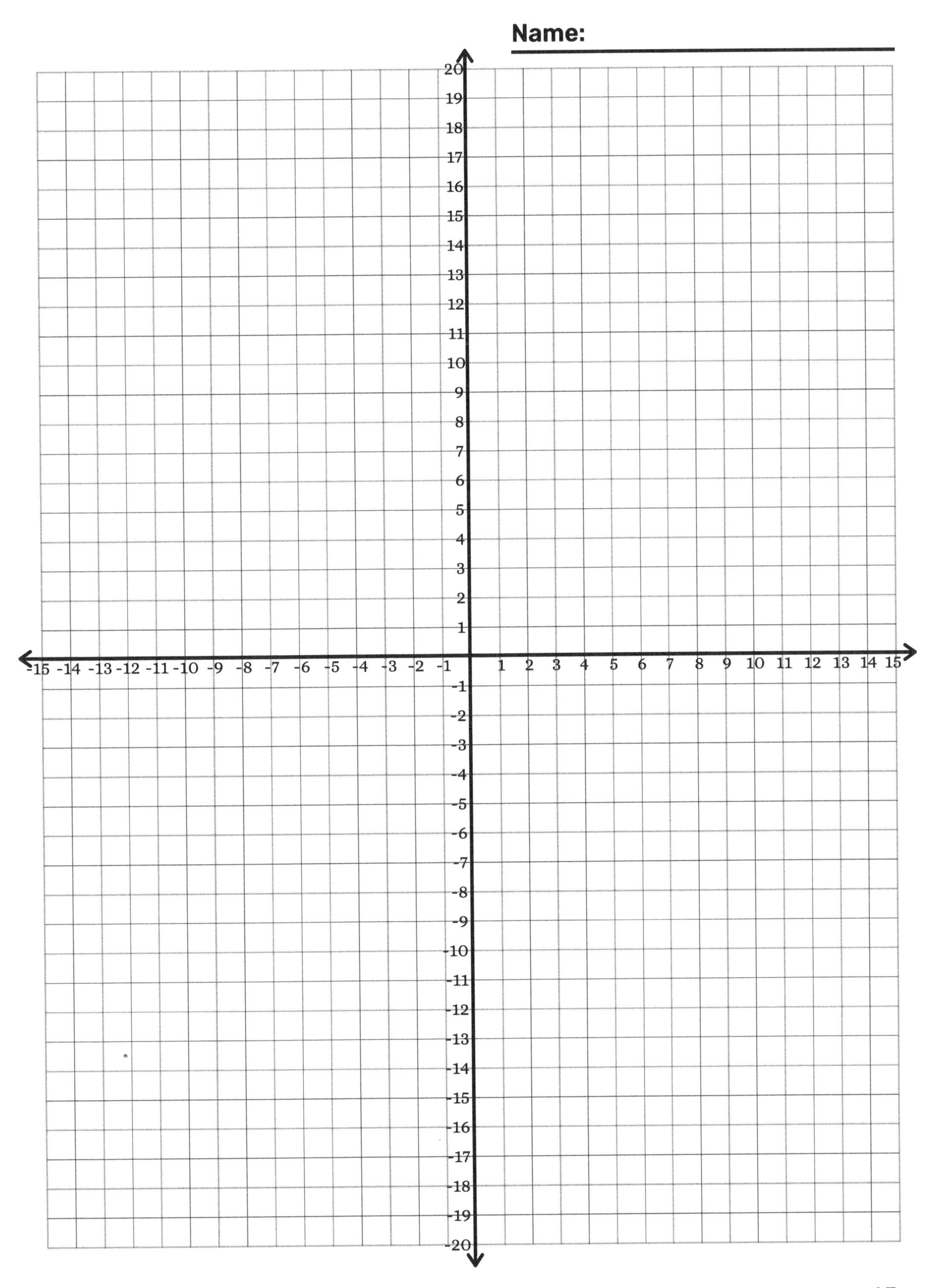

20
19
18
17
16
15
14
13
12
11
10
9
8
7
6
5
4
3
2
1
-15 -14 -13 -12 -11 -10 -9 -8 -7 -6 -5 -4 -3 -2 -1
1 2 3 4 5 6 7 8 9 10 11 12 13 14 15
-1
-2
-3
-4
-5
-6
-7
-8
-9
-10
-11
-12
-13
-14
-15
-16
-17
-18
-19
-20

PUPPY PALS MYSTERY PICTURE #1 (FIRST QUADRANT)

Plot the ordered pairs, connecting with straight lines as you go. Be sure to stop when you reach **"STOP"** and begin a new series of connected lines at each **"START"**. *Have fun!*

START
(12, 18)
(10, 16)
(10, 7)
(11, 6)
(10, 5)
(10, 4)
(11, 4)
(11, 5)
(11, 4)
(12, 4)
(12, 5)
(12, 4)
(13, 4)
(13, 5)
(13, 4)
(15, 4)
(15, 11)
(14, 12)
(15, 11)
(16, 12)
(15, 11)
(15, 4)
(17, 4)
(17, 5)
(17, 4)
(18, 4)
(18, 5)
(18, 4)
(19, 4)
(19, 5)
(19, 4)
(20, 4)
(20, 5)
(19, 6)
(20, 7)
(20, 16)
(18, 18)
STOP

START
(10, 15)
(8, 15)
(7, 14)
(7, 7)
(8, 6)
(7, 5)
(7, 4)
(8, 4)
(8, 5)
(8, 4)
(9, 4)
(9, 5)
(9, 4)
(10, 4)
STOP

START
(20, 15)
(22, 15)
(23, 14)
(23, 7)
(22, 6)
(23, 5)
(23, 4)
(22, 4)
(22, 5)
(22, 4)
(21, 4)
(21, 5)
(21, 4)
(20, 4)
STOP

START
(22, 6)
(26, 6)
(27, 7)
(27, 9)
(29, 9)
(29, 6)
(27, 4)
(23, 4)
STOP

START
(11, 26)
(11, 19)
(10, 18)
(8, 18)
(7, 19)
(7, 26)
(9, 28)
(12, 28)
(12, 27)
(18, 27)
(18, 28)
(21, 28)
(23, 26)
(23, 19)
(22, 18)
(20, 18)
(19, 19)
(19, 26)
(19, 19)
(17, 17)
(13, 17)
(11, 19)
STOP

START
(12, 29)
(18, 29)
STOP

START
(12, 28)
(12, 30)
(13, 30)
(11, 30)
(10, 31)
(10, 32)
(11, 33)
(12, 33)
(12, 32)
(12, 33)
(13, 34)
(17, 34)
(18, 33)
(18, 32)
(18, 33)
(19, 33)
(20, 32)
(20, 31)
(19, 30)
(17, 30)
(18, 30)
(18, 28)
STOP

START
(16, 25)
(17, 25)
(17, 24)
(16, 24)
(16, 26)
(17, 26)
(17, 25)
STOP

START
(13, 25)
(14, 25)
(14, 24)
(13, 24)
(13, 26)
(14, 26)
(14, 25)
STOP

START
(12, 20)
(14, 18)
(15, 19)
(15, 20)
(14, 20)
(13, 21)
(13, 22)
(14, 23)
(16, 23)
(17, 22)
(17, 21)
(16, 20)
(15, 20)
(15, 19)
(16, 18)
(18, 20)
STOP

START
(11, 17)
(12, 16)
(18, 16)
(19, 17)
STOP

START
(14, 16)
(13, 15)
(14, 14)
(14, 15)
(15, 16)
(16, 15)
(16, 14)
(17, 15)
(16, 16)
STOP

Name: ______________________

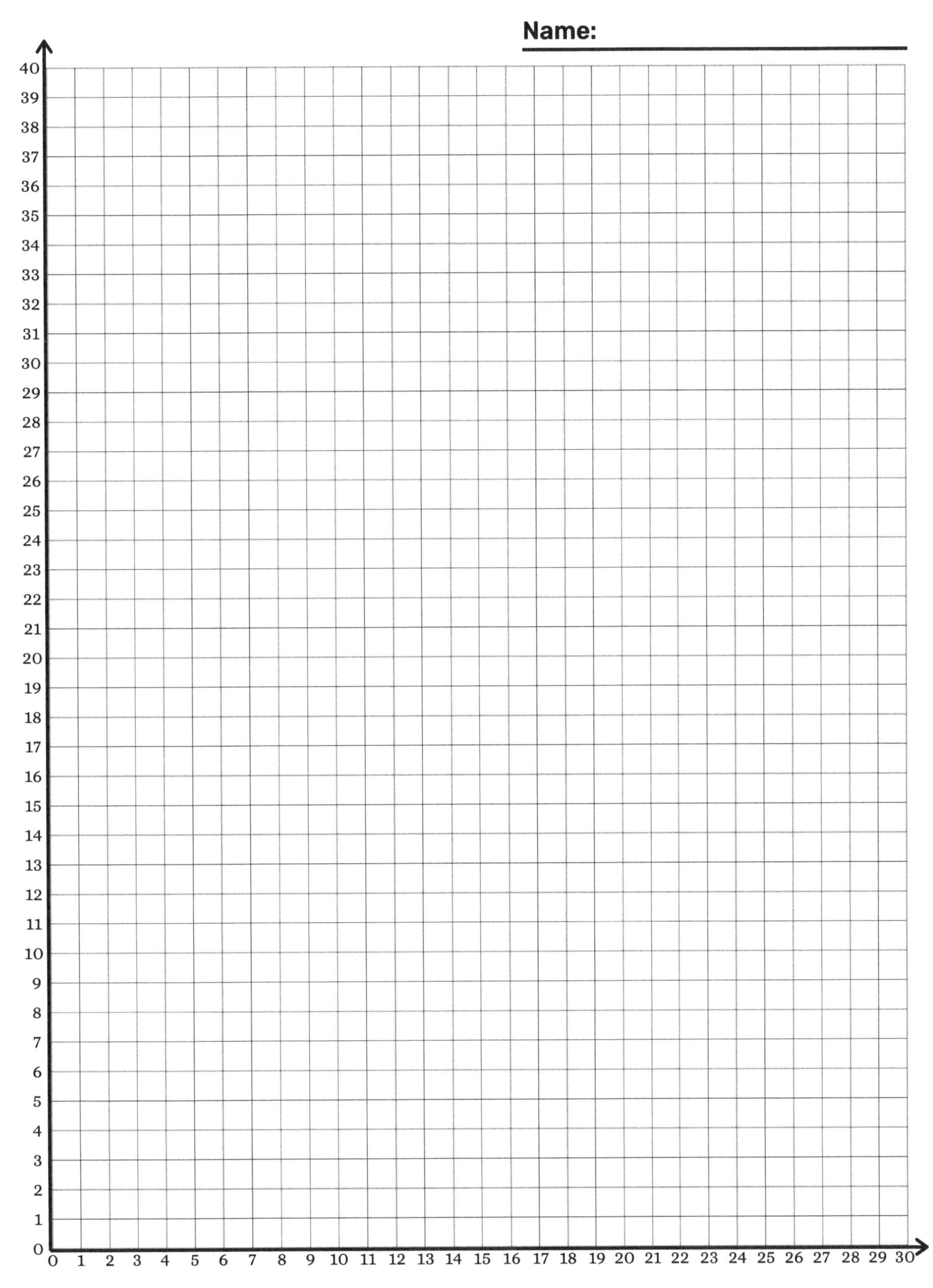

40
39
38
37
36
35
34
33
32
31
30
29
28
27
26
25
24
23
22
21
20
19
18
17
16
15
14
13
12
11
10
9
8
7
6
5
4
3
2
1
0
0 1 2 3 4 5 6 7 8 9 10 11 12 13 14 15 16 17 18 19 20 21 22 23 24 25 26 27 28 29 30

PUPPY PALS MYSTERY PICTURE #1 (FOUR QUADRANT)

Plot the ordered pairs, connecting with straight lines as you go. Be sure to stop when you reach **"STOP"** and begin a new series of connected lines at each **"START"**. *Have fun!*

START
(-3, -2)
(-5, -4)
(-5, -13)
(-4, -14)
(-5, -15)
(-5, -16)
(-4, -16)
(-4, -15)
(-4, -16)
(-3, -16)
(-3, -15)
(-3, -16)
(-2, -16)
(-2, -15)
(-2, -16)
(0, -16)
(0, -9)
(-1, -8)
(0, -9)
(1, -8)
(0, -9)
(0, -16)
(2, -16)
(2, -15)
(2, -16)
(3, -16)
(3, -15)
(3, -16)
(4, -16)
(4, -15)
(4, -16)
(5, -16)
(5, -15)
(4, -14)
(5, -13)
(5, -4)
(3, -2)
STOP

START
(-5, -5)
(-7, -5)
(-8, -6)
(-8, -13)
(-7, -14)
(-8, -15)
(-8, -16)
(-7, -16)
(-7, -15)
(-7, -16)
(-6, -16)
(-6, -15)
(-6, -16)
(-5, -16)
STOP

START
(5, -5)
(7, -5)
(8, -6)
(8, -13)
(7, -14)
(8, -15)
(8, -16)
(7, -16)
(7, -15)
(7, -16)
(6, -16)
(6, -15)
(6, -16)
(5, -16)
STOP

START
(7, -14)
(11, -14)
(12, -13)
(12, -11)
(14, -11)
(14, -14)
(12, -16)
(8, -16)
STOP

START
(-4, 6)
(-4, -1)
(-5, -2)
(-7, -2)
(-8, -1)
(-8, 6)
(-6, 8)
(-3, 8)
(-3, 7)
(3, 7)
(3, 8)
(6, 8)
(8, 6)
(8, -1)
(7, -2)
(5, -2)
(4, -1)
(4, 6)
(4, -1)
(2, -3)
(-2, -3)
(-4, -1)
STOP

START
(-3, 9)
(3, 9)
STOP

START
(-3, 8)
(-3, 10)
(-2, 10)
(-4, 10)
(-5, 11)
(-5, 12)
(-4, 13)
(-3, 13)
(-3, 12)
(-3, 13)
(-2, 14)
(2, 14)
(3, 13)
(3, 12)
(3, 13)
(4, 13)
(5, 12)
(5, 11)
(4, 10)
(2, 10)
(3, 10)
(3, 8)
STOP

START
(-2, 5)
(-1, 5)
(-1, 4)
(-2, 4)
(-2, 6)
(-1, 6)
(-1, 5)
STOP

START
(1, 5)
(2, 5)
(2, 4)
(1, 4)
(1, 6)
(2, 6)
(2, 5)
STOP

START
(-3, 0)
(-1, -2)
(0, -1)
(0, 0)
(-1, 0)
(-2, 1)
(-2, 2)
(-1, 3)
(1, 3)
(2, 2)
(2, 1)
(1, 0)
(0, 0)
(0, -1)
(1, -2)
(3, 0)
STOP

START
(-4, -3)
(-3, -4)
(3, -4)
(4, -3)
STOP

START
(-1, -4)
(-2, -5)
(-1, -6)
(-1, -5)
(0, -4)
(1, -5)
(1, -6)
(2, -5)
(1, -4)
STOP

Name: ______________________

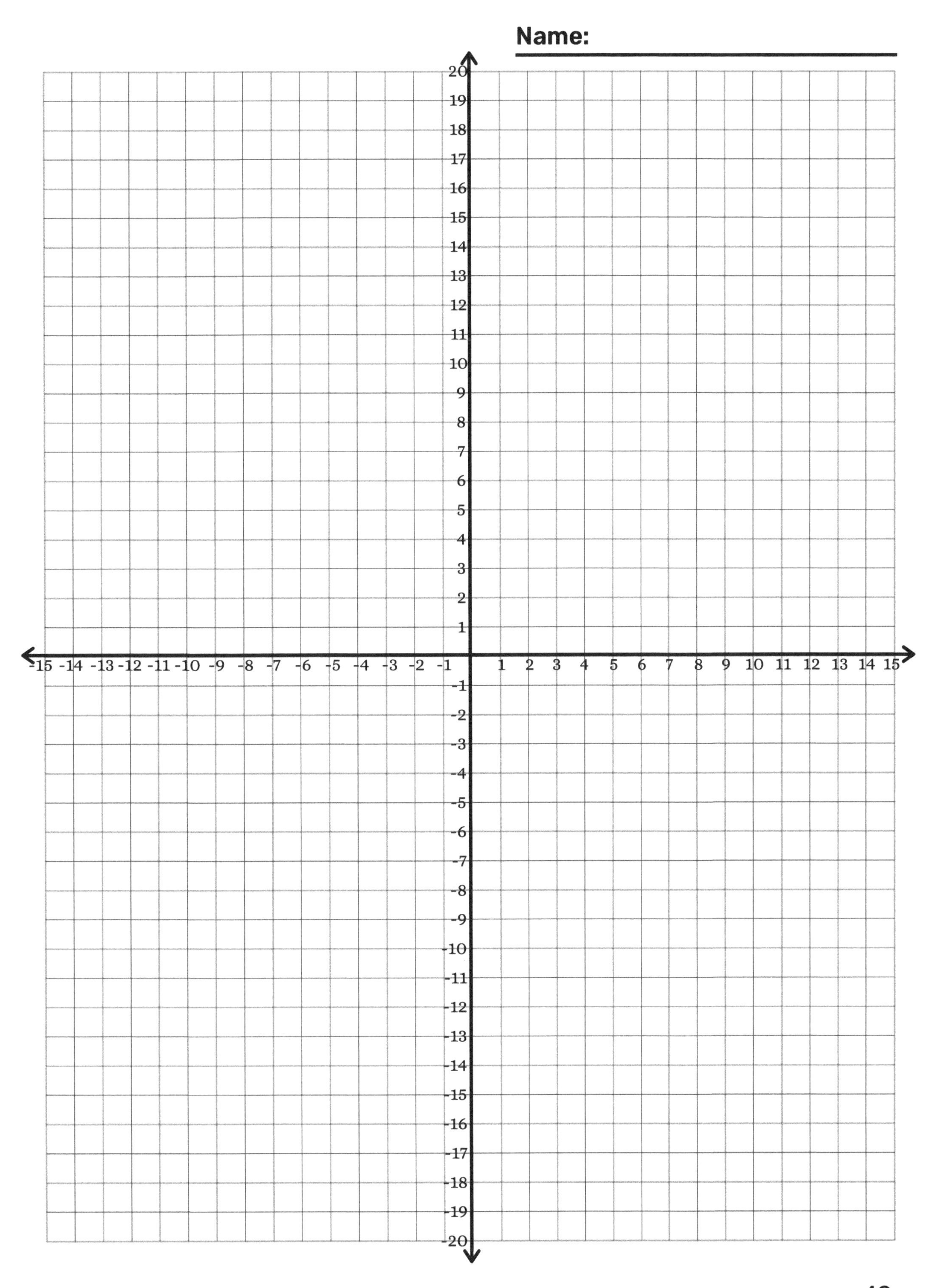

20
19
18
17
16
15
14
13
12
11
10
9
8
7
6
5
4
3
2
1
-15 -14 -13 -12 -11 -10 -9 -8 -7 -6 -5 -4 -3 -2 -1
1 2 3 4 5 6 7 8 9 10 11 12 13 14 15
-1
-2
-3
-4
-5
-6
-7
-8
-9
-10
-11
-12
-13
-14
-15
-16
-17
-18
-19
-20

PUPPY PALS MYSTERY PICTURE #2 (FIRST QUADRANT)

Plot the ordered pairs, connecting with straight lines as you go. Be sure to stop when you reach **"STOP"** and begin a new series of connected lines at each **"START"**. *Have fun!*

START (8, 12) (2, 12) (1, 11) (1, 10) (2, 9) (28, 9) (29, 10) (29, 11) (28, 12) (22, 12) **STOP** **START** (6, 9) (7, 8) (6, 7) (6, 6) (7, 5) (8, 5) (9, 6) (9, 7) (8, 8) (9, 9) **STOP** **START** (7, 9) (7, 8) (8, 8) (8, 9) **STOP**	**START** (7, 7) (7, 6) (8, 6) (8, 7) (7, 7) **STOP** **START** (21, 9) (22, 8) (21, 7) (21, 6) (22, 5) (23, 5) (24, 6) (24, 7) (23, 8) (24, 9) **STOP** **START** (22, 9) (22, 8) (23, 8) (23, 9) **STOP** **START** (22, 7) (22, 6) (23, 6) (23, 7) (22, 7) **STOP**	**START** (8, 22) (8, 19) (11, 16) (11, 17) (11, 14) (10, 13) (10, 11) (11, 10) (14, 10) (14, 16) (14, 15) (19, 15) (19, 16) (17, 18) (19, 16) (19, 14) (18, 13) (18, 11) (19, 10) (22, 10) (22, 21) (20, 23) (17, 23) **STOP** **START** (9, 18) (9, 15) (8, 14) (8, 12) (9, 11) (10, 11) **STOP** **START** (14, 12) (16, 12) **STOP**	**START** (17, 15) (16, 14) (16, 12) (17, 11) (18, 11) **STOP** **START** (22, 19) (24, 17) (27, 17) (29, 19) (29, 22) (26, 19) (22, 23) (20, 23) **STOP** **START** (11, 30) (10, 31) (7, 31) (5, 29) (3, 29) (2, 28) (2, 26) (6, 22) (10, 22) (12, 24) **STOP** **START** (13, 23) (11, 21) (8, 21) **STOP**	**START** (11, 30) (13, 30) (17, 26) (17, 23) (16, 22) (14, 22) (10, 26) (10, 29) (11, 30) **STOP** **START** (7, 26) (7, 25) (8, 25) (7, 25) (5, 23) **STOP** **START** (3, 29) (4, 28) (4, 27) (3, 26) (2, 27) **STOP** **START** (6, 29) (7, 29) (7, 28) (6, 28) (6, 30) (8, 30) (8, 28) (7, 28) **STOP**

Name: ____________________

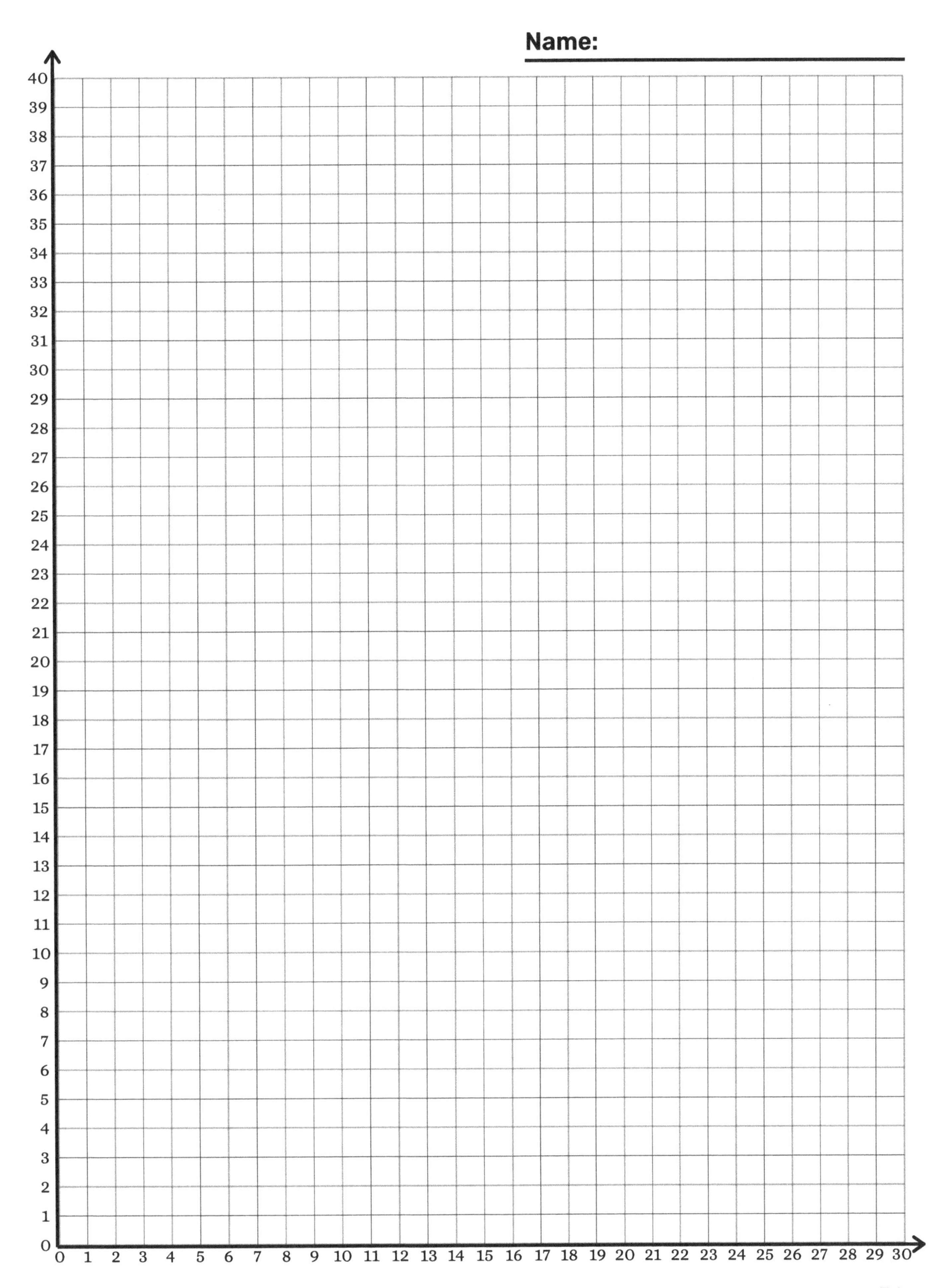

40
39
38
37
36
35
34
33
32
31
30
29
28
27
26
25
24
23
22
21
20
19
18
17
16
15
14
13
12
11
10
9
8
7
6
5
4
3
2
1
0
0 1 2 3 4 5 6 7 8 9 10 11 12 13 14 15 16 17 18 19 20 21 22 23 24 25 26 27 28 29 30

PUPPY PALS MYSTERY PICTURE #2 (FOUR QUADRANT)

Plot the ordered pairs, connecting with straight lines as you go. Be sure to stop when you reach **"STOP"** and begin a new series of connected lines at each **"START"**. *Have fun!*

START
(-7, -8)
(-13, -8)
(-14, -9)
(-14, -10)
(-13, -11)
(13, -11)
(14, -10)
(14, -9)
(13, -8)
(7, -8)
STOP

START
(-9, -11)
(-8, -12)
(-9, -13)
(-9, -14)
(-8, -15)
(-7, -15)
(-6, -14)
(-6, -13)
(-7, -12)
(-6, -11)
STOP

START
(-8, -11)
(-8, -12)
(-7, -12)
(-7, -11)
STOP

START
(-8, -13)
(-8, -14)
(-7, -14)
(-7, -13)
(-8, -13)
STOP

START
(6, -11)
(7, -12)
(6, -13)
(6, -14)
(7, -15)
(8, -15)
(9, -14)
(9, -13)
(8, -12)
(9, -11)
STOP

START
(7, -11)
(7, -12)
(8, -12)
(8, -11)
STOP

START
(7, -13)
(7, -14)
(8, -14)
(8, -13)
(7, -13)
STOP

START
(-7, 2)
(-7, -1)
(-4, -4)
(-4, -3)
(-4, -6)
(-5, -7)
(-5, -9)
(-4, -10)
(-1, -10)
(-1, -4)
(-1, -5)
(4, -5)
(4, -4)
(2, -2)
(4, -4)
(4, -6)
(3, -7)
(3, -9)
(4, -10)
(7, -10)
(7, 1)
(5, 3)
(2, 3)
STOP

START
(-6, -2)
(-6, -5)
(-7, -6)
(-7, -8)
(-6, -9)
(-5, -9)
STOP

START
(-1, -8)
(1, -8)
STOP

START
(2, -5)
(1, -6)
(1, -8)
(2, -9)
(3, -9)
STOP

START
(5, 3)
(7, 3)
(11, -1)
(14, 2)
(14, -1)
(12, -3)
(9, -3)
(7, -1)
STOP

START
(-4, 10)
(-5, 11)
(-8, 11)
(-10, 9)
(-12, 9)
(-13, 8)
(-13, 6)
(-9, 2)
(-5, 2)
(-3, 4)
STOP

START
(-2, 3)
(-4, 1)
(-7, 1)
STOP

START
(-4, 10)
(-2, 10)
(2, 6)
(2, 3)
(1, 2)
(-1, 2)
(-5, 6)
(-5, 9)
(-4, 10)
STOP

START
(-8, 6)
(-8, 5)
(-7, 5)
(-8, 5)
(-10, 3)
STOP

START
(-12, 9)
(-11, 8)
(-11, 7)
(-12, 6)
(-13, 7)
STOP

START
(-9, 9)
(-8, 9)
(-8, 8)
(-9, 8)
(-9, 10)
(-7, 10)
(-7, 8)
(-8, 8)
STOP

Name: ____________________

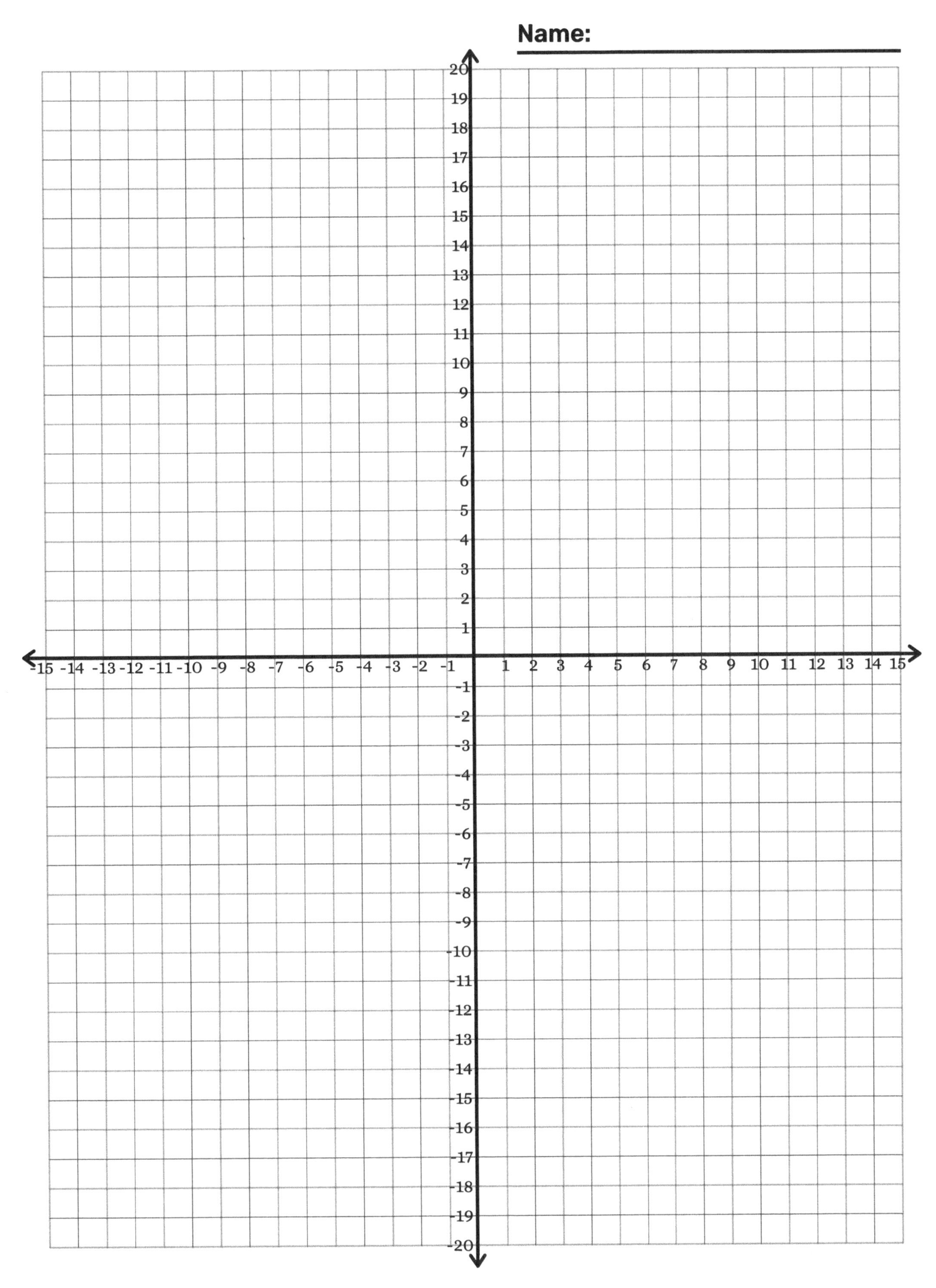

20
19
18
17
16
15
14
13
12
11
10
9
8
7
6
5
4
3
2
1
-15 -14 -13 -12 -11 -10 -9 -8 -7 -6 -5 -4 -3 -2 -1
1 2 3 4 5 6 7 8 9 10 11 12 13 14 15
-1
-2
-3
-4
-5
-6
-7
-8
-9
-10
-11
-12
-13
-14
-15
-16
-17
-18
-19
-20

PUPPY PALS MYSTERY PICTURE #3 (FIRST QUADRANT)

Plot the ordered pairs, connecting with straight lines as you go. Be sure to stop when you reach **"STOP"** and begin a new series of connected lines at each **"START"**. *Have fun!*

START
(22, 18)
(22, 26)
(19, 29)
(13, 29)
(10, 26)
(10, 18)
(11, 17)
(21, 17)
(22, 18)
STOP

START
(18, 29)
(18, 32)
(19, 33)
(21, 33)
(22, 32)
(22, 26)
(21, 27)
(21, 32)
(19, 32)
(19, 29)
STOP

START
(14, 29)
(14, 32)
(13, 33)
(11, 33)
(10, 32)
(10, 26)
(11, 27)
(11, 32)
(13, 32)
(13, 29)
STOP

START
(22, 18)
(24, 16)
(24, 12)
(25, 13)
(24, 12)
(24, 10)
(22, 8)
(20, 8)
(20, 13)
(20, 11)
(7, 11)
(5, 13)
(7, 11)
(8, 11)
(8, 15)
(8, 14)
(5, 17)
(5, 24)
(6, 25)
(8, 25)
(9, 24)
(9, 19)
(8, 20)
(10, 18)
STOP

START
(13, 24)
(13, 25)
(14, 25)
(14, 24)
(13, 24)
(12, 25)
(12, 26)
(13, 27)
(14, 27)
(15, 26)
(15, 25)
(14, 24)
STOP

START
(19, 24)
(19, 25)
(18, 25)
(18, 24)
(19, 24)
(20, 25)
(20, 26)
(19, 27)
(18, 27)
(17, 26)
(17, 25)
(18, 24)
STOP

START
(10, 19)
(15, 24)
(17, 24)
(22, 19)
STOP

START
(14, 23)
(14, 22)
(15, 21)
(17, 21)
(18, 22)
(18, 23)
STOP

START
(12, 19)
(13, 18)
(14, 18)
(16, 20)
(16, 21)
(16, 20)
(18, 18)
(19, 18)
(20, 19)
STOP

START
(15, 19)
(15, 17)
(16, 17)
(16, 18)
(16, 17)
(17, 17)
(17, 19)
STOP

START
(23, 17)
(25, 17)
(29, 13)
(29, 12)
(30, 12)
(29, 12)
(29, 8)
(25, 4)
(5, 4)
(1, 8)
(1, 12)
(0, 12)
(1, 12)
(1, 13)
(5, 17)
STOP

START
(25, 17)
(25, 15)
(26, 14)
(28, 14)
STOP

START
(29, 10)
(27, 10)
(26, 9)
(26, 7)
(27, 6)
STOP

START
(20, 4)
(21, 5)
(21, 7)
(20, 8)
(18, 8)
(17, 7)
(17, 5)
(18, 4)
STOP

START
(13, 6)
(14, 7)
(14, 9)
(13, 10)
(11, 10)
(10, 9)
(10, 7)
(11, 6)
(13, 6)
STOP

START
(8, 4)
(8, 5)
(7, 6)
(5, 6)
(4, 5)
STOP

START
(3, 12)
(2, 11)
(2, 9)
(3, 8)
(5, 8)
(6, 9)
(6, 11)
(5, 12)
(3, 12)
STOP

START
(2, 14)
(1, 15)
(2, 16)
(4, 14)
(6, 14)
(7, 15)
STOP

START
(6, 23)
(6, 22)
(7, 21)
(8, 22)
(8, 23)
(6, 23)
STOP

Dot at each Coordinate:
(6, 24)
(7, 24)
(8, 24)

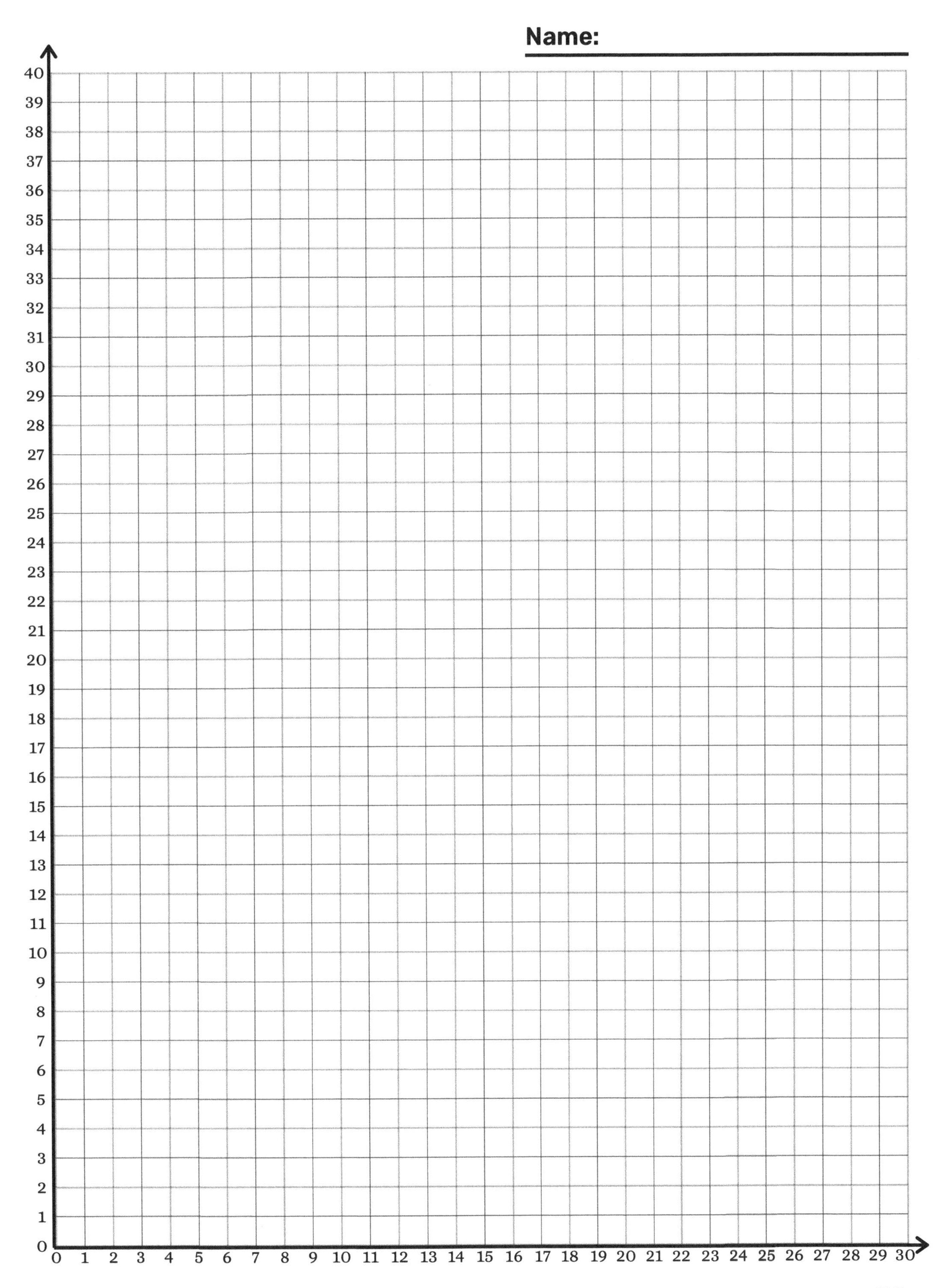
Name:
40 39 38 37 36 35 34 33 32 31 30 29 28 27 26 25 24 23 22 21 20 19 18 17 16 15 14 13 12 11 10 9 8 7 6 5 4 3 2 1 0
0 1 2 3 4 5 6 7 8 9 10 11 12 13 14 15 16 17 18 19 20 21 22 23 24 25 26 27 28 29 30

PUPPY PALS MYSTERY PICTURE #3 (FOUR QUADRANT)

Plot the ordered pairs, connecting with straight lines as you go. Be sure to stop when you reach **"STOP"** and begin a new series of connected lines at each **"START"**. *Have fun!*

START
(7, -2)
(7, 6)
(4, 9)
(-2, 9)
(-5, 6)
(-5, -2)
(-4, -3)
(6, -3)
(7, -2)
STOP

START
(3, 9)
(3, 12)
(4, 13)
(6, 13)
(7, 12)
(7, 6)
(6, 7)
(6, 12)
(4, 12)
(4, 9)
STOP

START
(-1, 9)
(-1, 12)
(-2, 13)
(-4, 13)
(-5, 12)
(-5, 6)
(-4, 7)
(-4, 12)
(-2, 12)
(-2, 9)
STOP

START
(7, -2)
(9, -4)
(9, -8)
(10, -7)
(9, -8)
(9, -10)
(7, -12)
(5, -12)
(5, -7)
(5, -9)
(-8, -9)
(-10, -7)
(-8, -9)
(-7, -9)
(-7, -5)
(-7, -6)
(-10, -3)
(-10, 4)
(-9, 5)
(-7, 5)
(-6, 4)
(-6, -1)
(-7, 0)
(-5, -2)
STOP

START
(-2, 4)
(-2, 5)
(-1, 5)
(-1, 4)
(-2, 4)
(-3, 5)
(-3, 6)
(-2, 7)
(-1, 7)
(0, 6)
(0, 5)
(-1, 4)
STOP

START
(4, 4)
(4, 5)
(3, 5)
(3, 4)
(4, 4)
(5, 5)
(5, 6)
(4, 7)
(3, 7)
(2, 6)
(2, 5)
(3, 4)
STOP

START
(-5, -1)
(0, 4)
(2, 4)
(7, -1)
STOP

START
(-1, 3)
(-1, 2)
(0, 1)
(2, 1)
(3, 2)
(3, 3)
STOP

START
(-3, -1)
(-2, -2)
(-1, -2)
(1, 0)
(1, 1)
(1, 0)
(3, -2)
(4, -2)
(5, -1)
STOP

START
(0, -1)
(0, -3)
(1, -3)
(1, -2)
(1, -3)
(2, -3)
(2, -1)
STOP

START
(8, -3)
(10, -3)
(14, -7)
(14, -8)
(15, -8)
(14, -8)
(14, -12)
(10, -16)
(-10, -16)
(-14, -12)
(-14, -8)
(-15, -8)
(-14, -8)
(-14, -7)
(-10, -3)
STOP

START
(10, -3)
(10, -5)
(11, -6)
(13, -6)
STOP

START
(14, -10)
(12, -10)
(11, -11)
(11, -13)
(12, -14)
STOP

START
(5, -16)
(6, -15)
(6, -13)
(5, -12)
(3, -12)
(2, -13)
(2, -15)
(3, -16)
STOP

START
(-4, -10)
(-2, -10)
(-1, -11)
(-1, -13)
(-2, -14)
(-4, -14)
(-5, -13)
(-5, -11)
(-4, -10)
STOP

START
(-7, -16)
(-7, -15)
(-8, -14)
(-10, -14)
(-11, -15)
STOP

START
(-12, -8)
(-10, -8)
(-9, -9)
(-9, -11)
(-10, -12)
(-12, -12)
(-13, -11)
(-13, -9)
(-12, -8)
STOP

START
(-13, -6)
(-14, -5)
(-13, -4)
(-11, -6)
(-9, -6)
(-8, -5)
STOP

START
(-9, 3)
(-7, 3)
(-7, 2)
(-8, 1)
(-9, 2)
(-9, 3)
STOP

Dot at each Coordinate:
(-9, 4)
(-8, 4)
(-7, 4)

Name: ______________________

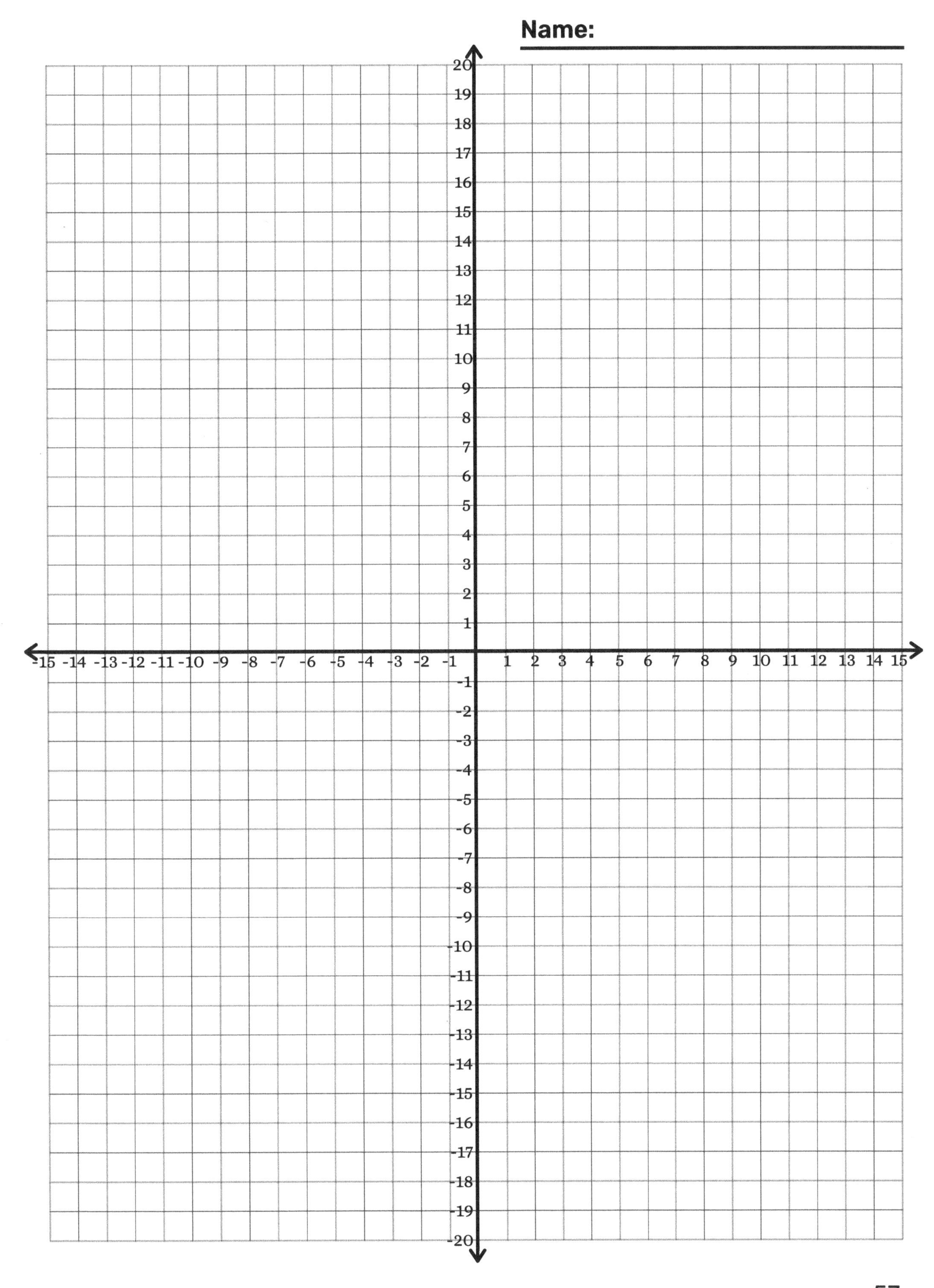

20
19
18
17
16
15
14
13
12
11
10
9
8
7
6
5
4
3
2
1
-15 -14 -13 -12 -11 -10 -9 -8 -7 -6 -5 -4 -3 -2 -1
1 2 3 4 5 6 7 8 9 10 11 12 13 14 15
-1
-2
-3
-4
-5
-6
-7
-8
-9
-10
-11
-12
-13
-14
-15
-16
-17
-18
-19
-20

PUPPY PALS MYSTERY PICTURE #4 (FIRST QUADRANT)

Plot the ordered pairs, connecting with straight lines as you go. Be sure to stop when you reach **"STOP"** and begin a new series of connected lines at each **"START"**. *Have fun!*

START
(0, 15)
(0, 12)
(2, 10)
(5, 10)
(7, 12)
(7, 15)
(5, 17)
(2, 17)
(0, 15)
STOP

START
(0, 14)
(1, 13)
(6, 13)
(7, 14)
STOP

START
(2, 17)
(3, 16)
(3, 11)
(2, 10)
STOP

START
(4, 17)
(5, 16)
(5, 11)
(4, 10)
STOP

START
(12, 27)
(11, 26)
(10, 26)
(10, 8)
(14, 8)
(14, 10)
(15, 11)
(16, 10)
(16, 8)
(20, 8)
(20, 26)
(19, 26)
(18, 27)
(18, 25)
(17, 24)
(13, 24)
(12, 25)
(12, 27)
STOP

START
(10, 26)
(9, 26)
(4, 21)
(2, 21)
(2, 19)
(3, 19)
(3, 20)
(3, 19)
(4, 19)
(4, 20)
(4, 19)
(5, 19)
(9, 23)
(10, 23)
STOP

START
(20, 26)
(21, 26)
(22, 25)
(22, 17)
(23, 16)
(23, 15)
(22, 15)
(22, 16)
(22, 15)
(21, 15)
(21, 16)
(21, 15)
(20, 15)
STOP

START
(20, 14)
(24, 14)
(25, 15)
(25, 17)
(27, 17)
(27, 14)
(25, 12)
(20, 12)
STOP

START
(11, 8)
(11, 4)
(12, 3)
(11, 2)
(11, 1)
(12, 1)
(12, 2)
(12, 1)
(13, 1)
(13, 2)
(13, 1)
(14, 1)
(14, 8)
STOP

START
(19, 8)
(19, 4)
(18, 3)
(19, 2)
(19, 1)
(18, 1)
(18, 2)
(18, 1)
(17, 1)
(17, 2)
(17, 1)
(16, 1)
(16, 8)
STOP

START
(14, 23)
(16, 23)
(17, 22)
(17, 17)
(16, 16)
(14, 16)
(13, 17)
(13, 22)
(14, 23)
STOP

START
(14, 22)
(16, 22)
(16, 17)
(14, 17)
(14, 22)
STOP

START
(11, 34)
(11, 28)
(10, 27)
(9, 27)
(8, 28)
(8, 35)
(10, 37)
(11, 37)
(12, 38)
(18, 38)
(19, 37)
(20, 37)
(22, 35)
(22, 28)
(21, 27)
(20, 27)
(19, 28)
(19, 34)
(19, 28)
(17, 26)
(13, 26)
(11, 28)
STOP

START
(11, 36)
(19, 36)
(19, 35)
(11, 35)
(11, 36)
STOP

START
(12, 33)
(14, 33)
(14, 32)
(12, 32)
(12, 34)
(14, 34)
(14, 33)
STOP

START
(16, 33)
(18, 33)
(18, 32)
(16, 32)
(16, 34)
(18, 34)
(18, 33)
STOP

START
(13, 29)
(13, 28)
(12, 28)
(13, 28)
(14, 27)
(15, 27)
(15, 29)
(13, 31)
(17, 31)
(15, 29)
(15, 27)
(16, 27)
(17, 28)
(17, 29)
(17, 28)
(18, 28)
STOP

START
(10, 15)
(20, 15)
STOP

Name: ____________________

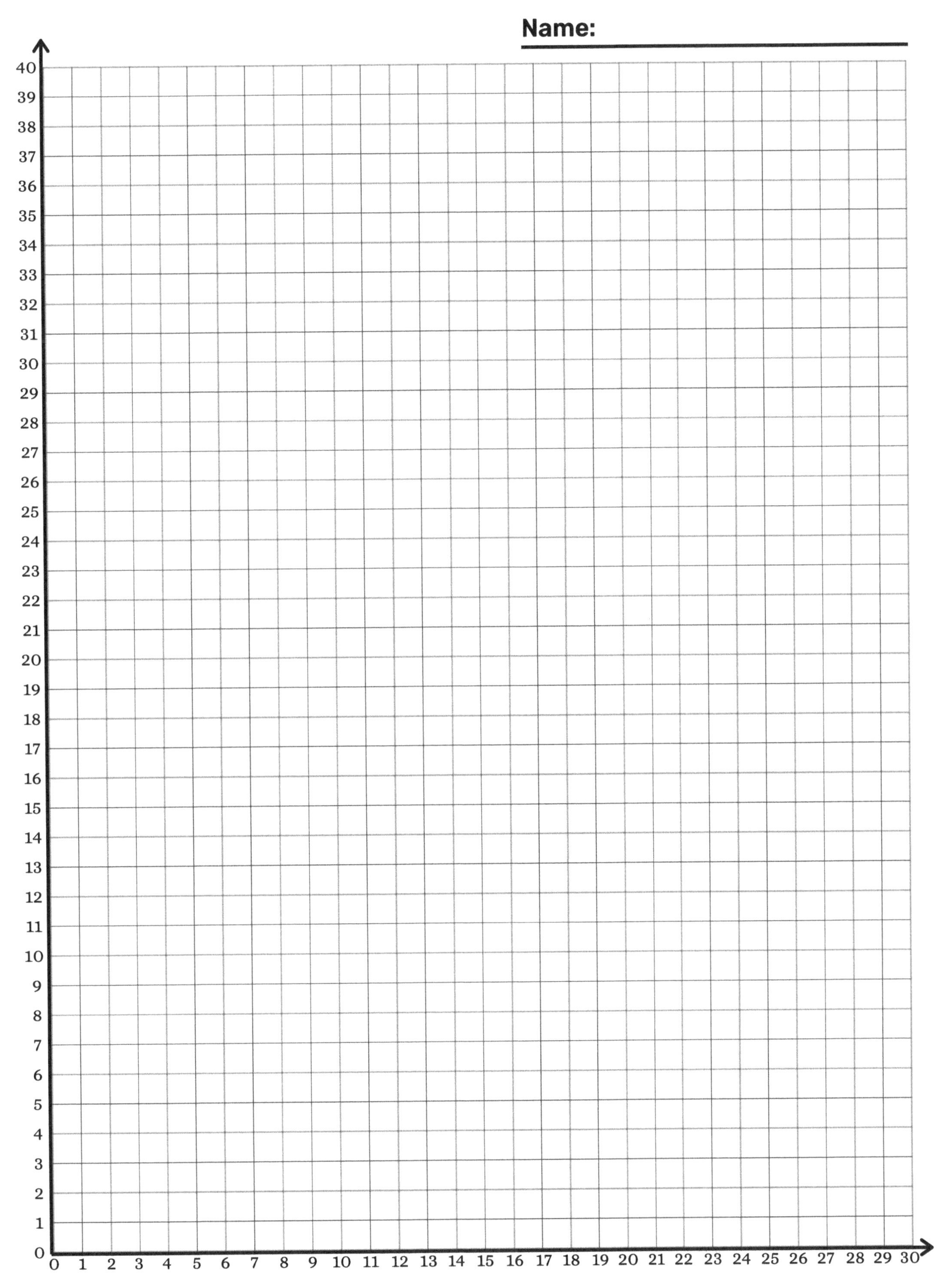

40
39
38
37
36
35
34
33
32
31
30
29
28
27
26
25
24
23
22
21
20
19
18
17
16
15
14
13
12
11
10
9
8
7
6
5
4
3
2
1
0
0 1 2 3 4 5 6 7 8 9 10 11 12 13 14 15 16 17 18 19 20 21 22 23 24 25 26 27 28 29 30

PUPPY PALS MYSTERY PICTURE #4 (FOUR QUADRANT)

Plot the ordered pairs, connecting with straight lines as you go. Be sure to stop when you reach **"STOP"** and begin a new series of connected lines at each **"START"**. *Have fun!*

START
(-15, -5)
(-15, -8)
(-13, -10)
(-10, -10)
(-8, -8)
(-8, -5)
(-10, -3)
(-13, -3)
(-15, -5)
STOP

START
(-15, -6)
(-14, -7)
(-9, -7)
(-8, -6)
STOP

START
(-13, -3)
(-12, -4)
(-12, -9)
(-13, -10)
STOP

START
(-11, -3)
(-10, -4)
(-10, -9)
(-11, -10)
STOP

START
(-3, 7)
(-4, 6)
(-5, 6)
(-5, -12)
(-1, -12)
(-1, -10)
(0, -9)
(1, -10)
(1, -12)
(5, -12)
(5, 6)
(4, 6)
(3, 7)
(3, 5)
(2, 4)
(-2, 4)
(-3, 5)
(-3, 7)
STOP

START
(-5, 6)
(-6, 6)
(-11, 1)
(-13, 1)
(-13, -1)
(-12, -1)
(-12, 0)
(-12, -1)
(-11, -1)
(-11, 0)
(-11, -1)
(-10, -1)
(-6, 3)
(-5, 3)
STOP

START
(5, 6)
(6, 6)
(7, 5)
(7, -3)
(8, -4)
(8, -5)
(7, -5)
(7, -4)
(7, -5)
(6, -5)
(6, -4)
(6, -5)
(5, -5)
STOP

START
(5, -6)
(9, -6)
(10, -5)
(10, -3)
(12, -3)
(12, -6)
(10, -8)
(5, -8)
STOP

START
(-4, -12)
(-4, -16)
(-3, -17)
(-4, -18)
(-4, -19)
(-3, -19)
(-3, -18)
(-3, -19)
(-2, -19)
(-2, -18)
(-2, -19)
(-1, -19)
(-1, -12)
STOP

START
(4, -12)
(4, -16)
(3, -17)
(4, -18)
(4, -19)
(3, -19)
(3, -18)
(3, -19)
(2, -19)
(2, -18)
(2, -19)
(1, -19)
(1, -12)
STOP

START
(-1, 3)
(1, 3)
(2, 2)
(2, -3)
(1, -4)
(-1, -4)
(-2, -3)
(-2, 2)
(-1, 3)
STOP

START
(-1, 2)
(1, 2)
(1, -3)
(-1, -3)
(-1, 2)
STOP

START
(-4, 14)
(-4, 8)
(-5, 7)
(-6, 7)
(-7, 8)
(-7, 15)
(-5, 17)
(-4, 17)
(-3, 18)
(3, 18)
(4, 17)
(5, 17)
(7, 15)
(7, 8)
(6, 7)
(5, 7)
(4, 8)
(4, 14)
(4, 8)
(2, 6)
(-2, 6)
(-4, 8)
STOP

START
(-4, 16)
(4, 16)
(4, 15)
(-4, 15)
(-4, 16)
STOP

START
(-3, 13)
(-1, 13)
(-1, 12)
(-3, 12)
(-3, 14)
(-1, 14)
(-1, 13)
STOP

START
(1, 13)
(3, 13)
(3, 12)
(1, 12)
(1, 14)
(3, 14)
(3, 13)
STOP

START
(-3, 8)
(-2, 8)
(-2, 9)
(-2, 8)
(-1, 7)
(0, 7)
(0, 9)
(-2, 11)
(2, 11)
(0, 9)
(0, 7)
(1, 7)
(2, 8)
(2, 9)
(2, 8)
(3, 8)
STOP

START
(-5, -5)
(5, -5)
STOP

Name: ______________________________

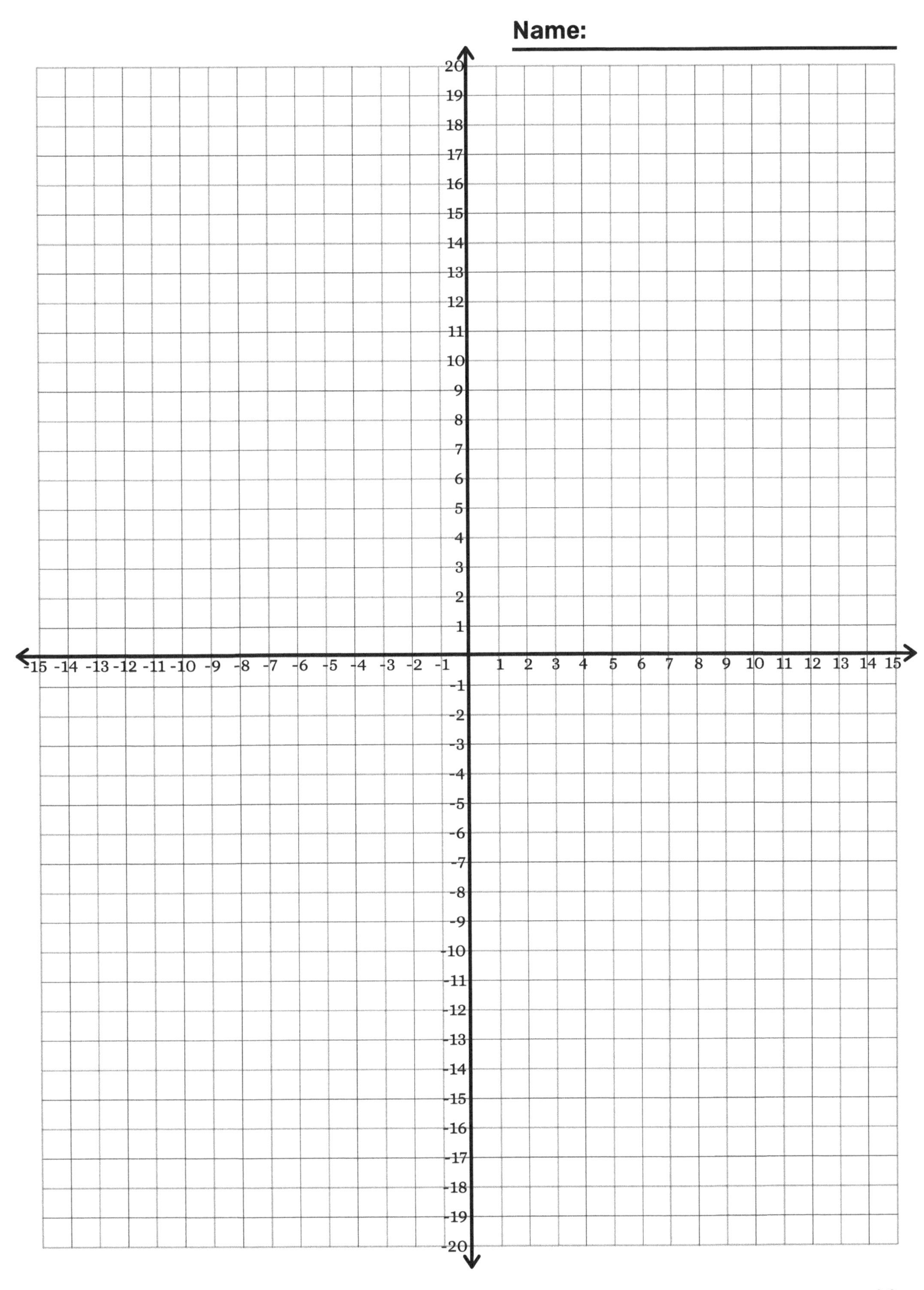
20 19 18 17 16 15 14 13 12 11 10 9 8 7 6 5 4 3 2 1
-15 -14 -13 -12 -11 -10 -9 -8 -7 -6 -5 -4 -3 -2 -1
1 2 3 4 5 6 7 8 9 10 11 12 13 14 15
-1 -2 -3 -4 -5 -6 -7 -8 -9 -10 -11 -12 -13 -14 -15 -16 -17 -18 -19 -20

SUMMER MYSTERY PICTURE #1 (FIRST QUADRANT)

Plot the ordered pairs, connecting with straight lines as you go. Be sure to stop when you reach **"STOP"** and begin a new series of connected lines at each **"START"**. *Have fun!*

<table>
<tr>
<td>**START**
(10, 12)
(11, 12)
(12, 11)
(12, 1)
(19, 1)
(19, 11)
(20, 12)
(21, 12)
(21, 15)
(23, 17)
(23, 18)
(22, 19)
(21, 19)
(21, 21)
(20, 22)
(22, 22)
(23, 23)
(23, 24)
(22, 25)
(21, 25)
(21, 27)
(20, 28)
(22, 28)
(23, 29)
(23, 30)
(22, 31)
(21, 31)
(21, 33)
(19, 35)
(17, 35)
(16, 34)
(14, 34)</td>
<td>(13, 35)
(12, 35)
(10, 33)
(10, 31)
(9, 31)
(8, 30)
(8, 29)
(9, 28)
(11, 28)
(10, 27)
(10, 25)
(9, 25)
(8, 24)
(8, 23)
(9, 22)
(11, 22)
(10, 21)
(10, 19)
(9, 19)
(8, 18)
(8, 17)
(10, 15)
(10, 12)
STOP

START
(10, 15)
(21, 15)
(22, 16)
(9, 16)
STOP

START
(11, 12)
(20, 12)
STOP</td>
<td>**START**
(11, 22)
(20, 22)
STOP

START
(11, 28)
(20, 28)
STOP

START
(16, 39)
(15, 39)
(15, 37)
(16, 37)
(17, 36)
(17, 35)
(16, 34)
(14, 34)
(13, 35)
(13, 36)
(14, 37)
(15, 37)
STOP

START
(12, 33)
(13, 34)
STOP

START
(12, 31)
(13, 32)
STOP

START
(14, 33)
(15, 34)
STOP</td>
<td>**START**
(15, 31)
(16, 32)
STOP

START
(17, 33)
(18, 32)
STOP

START
(19, 34)
(20, 33)
STOP

START
(19, 32)
(20, 31)
STOP

START
(13, 11)
(13, 9)
(14, 9)
STOP

START
(15, 11)
(15, 9)
(16, 9)
STOP

START
(17, 11)
(17, 9)
(18, 9)
STOP</td>
<td>**START**
(13, 8)
(13, 6)
(14, 6)
STOP

START
(15, 8)
(15, 6)
(16, 6)
STOP

START
(17, 8)
(17, 6)
(18, 6)
STOP

START
(13, 5)
(13, 3)
(14, 3)
STOP

START
(15, 5)
(15, 3)
(16, 3)
STOP

START
(17, 5)
(17, 3)
(18, 3)
STOP</td>
</tr>
</table>

Name: ____________________

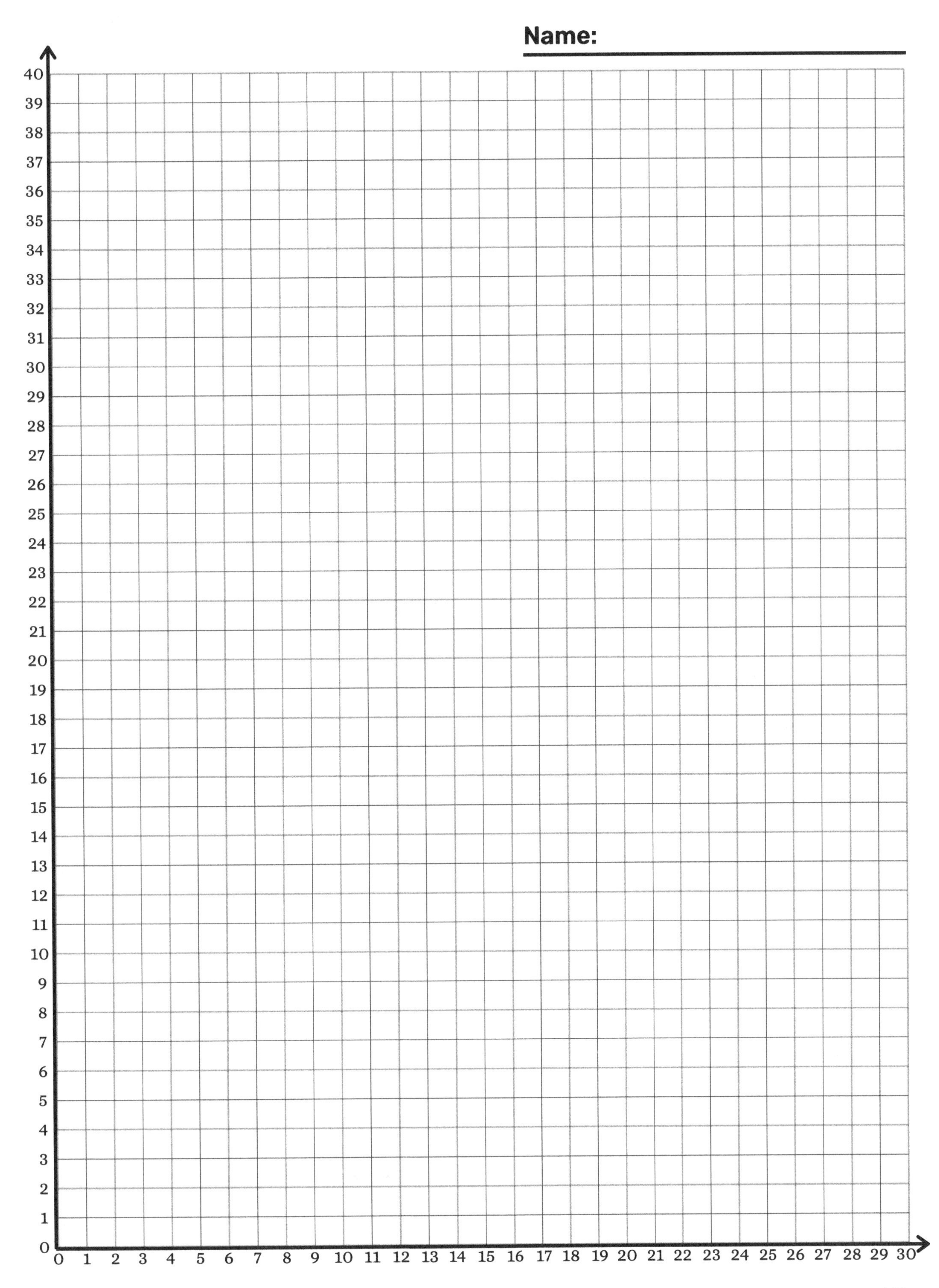

0 1 2 3 4 5 6 7 8 9 10 11 12 13 14 15 16 17 18 19 20 21 22 23 24 25 26 27 28 29 30
0 1 2 3 4 5 6 7 8 9 10 11 12 13 14 15 16 17 18 19 20 21 22 23 24 25 26 27 28 29 30 31 32 33 34 35 36 37 38 39 40

SUMMER MYSTERY PICTURE #1 (FOUR QUADRANT)

Plot the ordered pairs, connecting with straight lines as you go. Be sure to stop when you reach **"STOP"** and begin a new series of connected lines at each **"START"**. *Have fun!*

<table>
<tr>
<td>**START**
(-5, -8)
(-4, -8)
(-3, -9)
(-3, -19)
(4, -19)
(4, -9)
(5, -8)
(6, -8)
(6, -5)
(8, -3)
(8, -2)
(7, -1)
(6, -1)
(6, 1)
(5, 2)
(7, 2)
(8, 3)
(8, 4)
(7, 5)
(6, 5)
(6, 7)
(5, 8)
(7, 8)
(8, 9)
(8, 10)
(7, 11)
(6, 11)
(6, 13)
(4, 15)
(2, 15)
(1, 14)
(-1, 14)
(-2, 15)
(-3, 15)</td>
<td>(-5, 13)
(-5, 11)
(-6, 11)
(-7, 10)
(-7, 9)
(-6, 8)
(-4, 8)
(-5, 7)
(-5, 5)
(-6, 5)
(-7, 4)
(-7, 3)
(-6, 2)
(-4, 2)
(-5, 1)
(-5, -1)
(-6, -1)
(-7, -2)
(-7, -3)
(-5, -5)
(-5, -8)
STOP

START
(-5, -5)
(6, -5)
(7, -4)
(-6, -4)
STOP

START
(-4, -8)
(5, -8)
STOP</td>
<td>**START**
(-4, 2)
(5, 2)
STOP

START
(-4, 8)
(5, 8)
STOP

START
(1, 19)
(0, 19)
(0, 17)
(1, 17)
(2, 16)
(2, 15)
(1, 14)
(-1, 14)
(-2, 15)
(-2, 16)
(-1, 17)
(0, 17)
STOP

START
(-3, 13)
(-2, 14)
STOP

START
(-3, 11)
(-2, 12)
STOP

START
(-1, 13)
(0, 14)
STOP</td>
<td>**START**
(0, 11)
(1, 12)
STOP

START
(2, 13)
(3, 12)
STOP

START
(4, 14)
(5, 13)
STOP

START
(4, 12)
(5, 11)
STOP

START
(-2, -9)
(-2, -11)
(-1, -11)
STOP

START
(0, -9)
(0, -11)
(1, -11)
STOP

START
(2, -9)
(2, -11)
(3, -11)
STOP</td>
<td>**START**
(-2, -12)
(-2, -14)
(-1, -14)
STOP

START
(0, -12)
(0, -14)
(1, -14)
STOP

START
(2, -12)
(2, -14)
(3, -14)
STOP

START
(-2, -15)
(-2, -17)
(-1, -17)
STOP

START
(0, -15)
(0, -17)
(1, -17)
STOP

START
(2, -15)
(2, -17)
(3, -17)
STOP</td>
</tr>
</table>

Name: ______________________

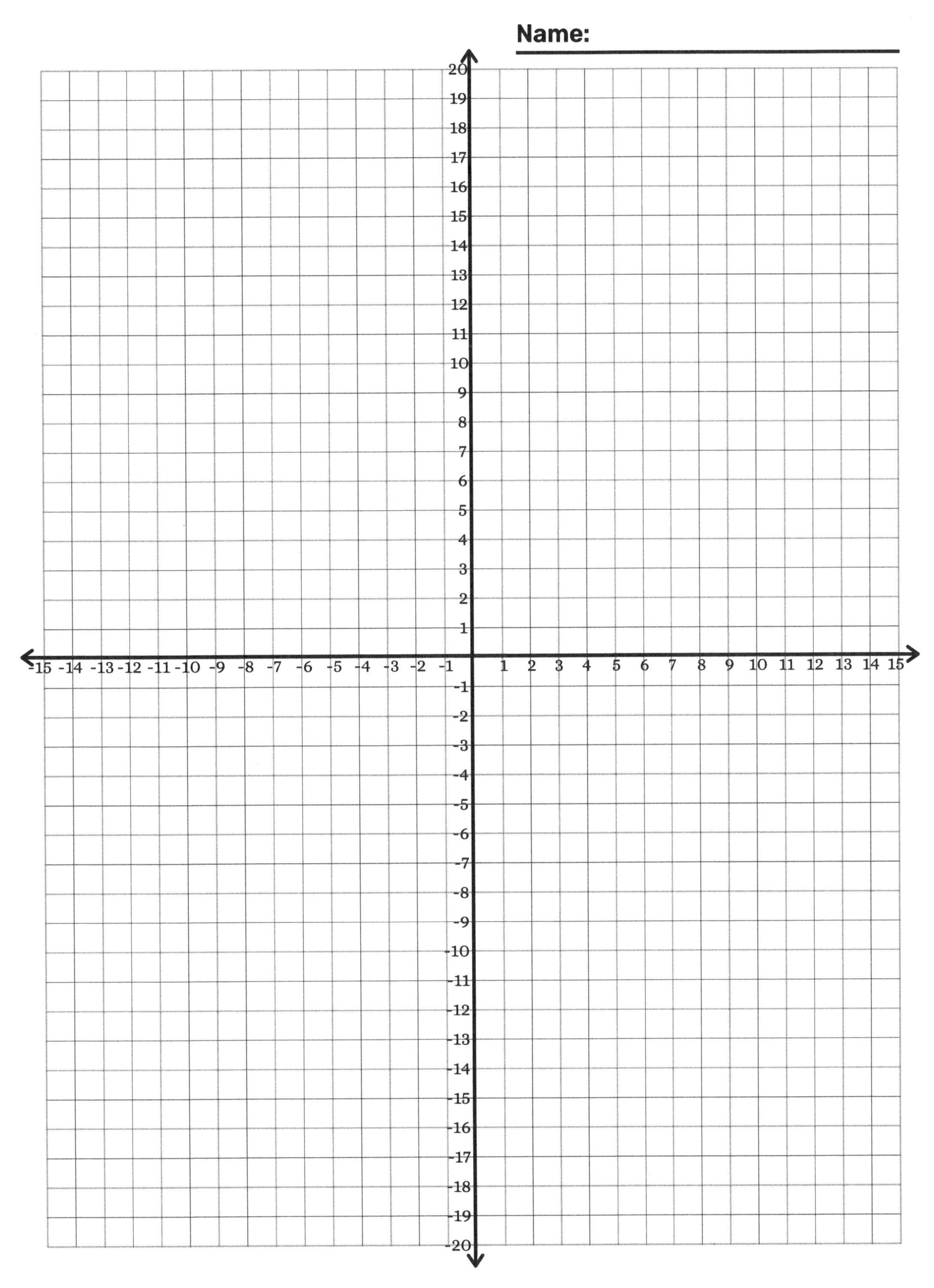

20
19
18
17
16
15
14
13
12
11
10
9
8
7
6
5
4
3
2
1
-15 -14 -13 -12 -11 -10 -9 -8 -7 -6 -5 -4 -3 -2 -1
1 2 3 4 5 6 7 8 9 10 11 12 13 14 15
-1
-2
-3
-4
-5
-6
-7
-8
-9
-10
-11
-12
-13
-14
-15
-16
-17
-18
-19
-20

SUMMER MYSTERY PICTURE #2 (FIRST QUADRANT)

Plot the ordered pairs, connecting with straight lines as you go. Be sure to stop when you reach **"STOP"** and begin a new series of connected lines at each **"START"**. *Have fun!*

START
(11, 18)
(14, 21)
(14, 32)
(12, 34)
(8, 34)
(6, 32)
(6, 29)
(8, 27)
(10, 27)
(10, 23)
(3, 16)
(3, 11)
(7, 7)
(23, 7)
(27, 11)
(27, 16)
(24, 19)
(12, 19)
STOP

START
(6, 29)
(4, 27)
(8, 27)
(7, 26)
(7, 22)
(4, 25)
(4, 27)
STOP

START
(20, 16)
(22, 14)
(21, 13)
(11, 13)
(10, 14)
(12, 16)
(20, 16)
STOP

START
(20, 12)
(21, 11)
(18, 8)
(12, 8)
(11, 9)
(11, 11)
(12, 12)
(20, 12)
STOP

START
(0, 17)
(4, 17)
STOP

START
(26, 17)
(30, 17)
STOP

START
(23, 37)
(26, 37)
(28, 35)
(28, 32)
(26, 30)
(23, 30)
(21, 32)
(21, 35)
(23, 37)
STOP

START
(8, 31)
(9, 32)
(10, 31)
(8, 31)
(9, 30)
(10, 31)
STOP

Name: ______________________

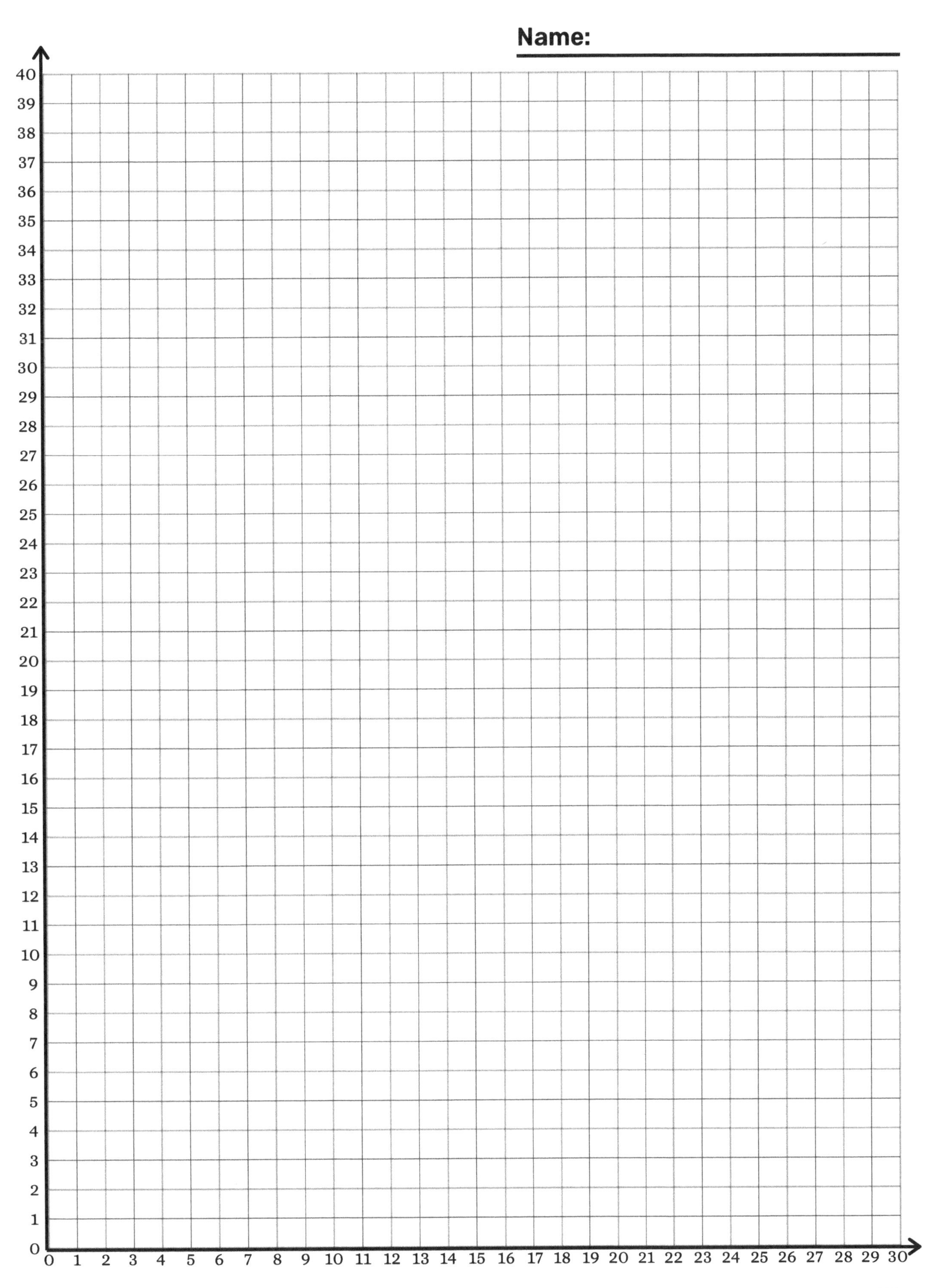

40
39
38
37
36
35
34
33
32
31
30
29
28
27
26
25
24
23
22
21
20
19
18
17
16
15
14
13
12
11
10
9
8
7
6
5
4
3
2
1
0
0 1 2 3 4 5 6 7 8 9 10 11 12 13 14 15 16 17 18 19 20 21 22 23 24 25 26 27 28 29 30

SUMMER MYSTERY PICTURE #2 (FOUR QUADRANT)

Plot the ordered pairs, connecting with straight lines as you go. Be sure to stop when you reach **"STOP"** and begin a new series of connected lines at each **"START"**. *Have fun!*

START
(-4, -2)
(-1, 1)
(-1, 12)
(-3, 14)
(-7, 14)
(-9, 12)
(-9, 9)
(-7, 7)
(-5, 7)
(-5, 3)
(-12, -4)
(-12, -9)
(-8, -13)
(8, -13)
(12, -9)
(12, -4)
(9, -1)
(-3, -1)
STOP

START
(-9, 9)
(-11, 7)
(-7, 7)
(-8, 6)
(-8, 2)
(-11, 5)
(-11, 7)
STOP

START
(5, -4)
(7, -6)
(6, -7)
(-4, -7)
(-5, -6)
(-3, -4)
(5, -4)
STOP

START
(5, -8)
(6, -9)
(3, -12)
(-3, -12)
(-4, -11)
(-4, -9)
(-3, -8)
(5, -8)
STOP

START
(-15, -3)
(-11, -3)
STOP

START
(11, -3)
(15, -3)
STOP

START
(8, 17)
(11, 17)
(13, 15)
(13, 12)
(11, 10)
(8, 10)
(6, 12)
(6, 15)
(8, 17)
STOP

START
(-7, 11)
(-6, 12)
(-5, 11)
(-7, 11)
(-6, 10)
(-5, 11)
STOP

Name: ______________________

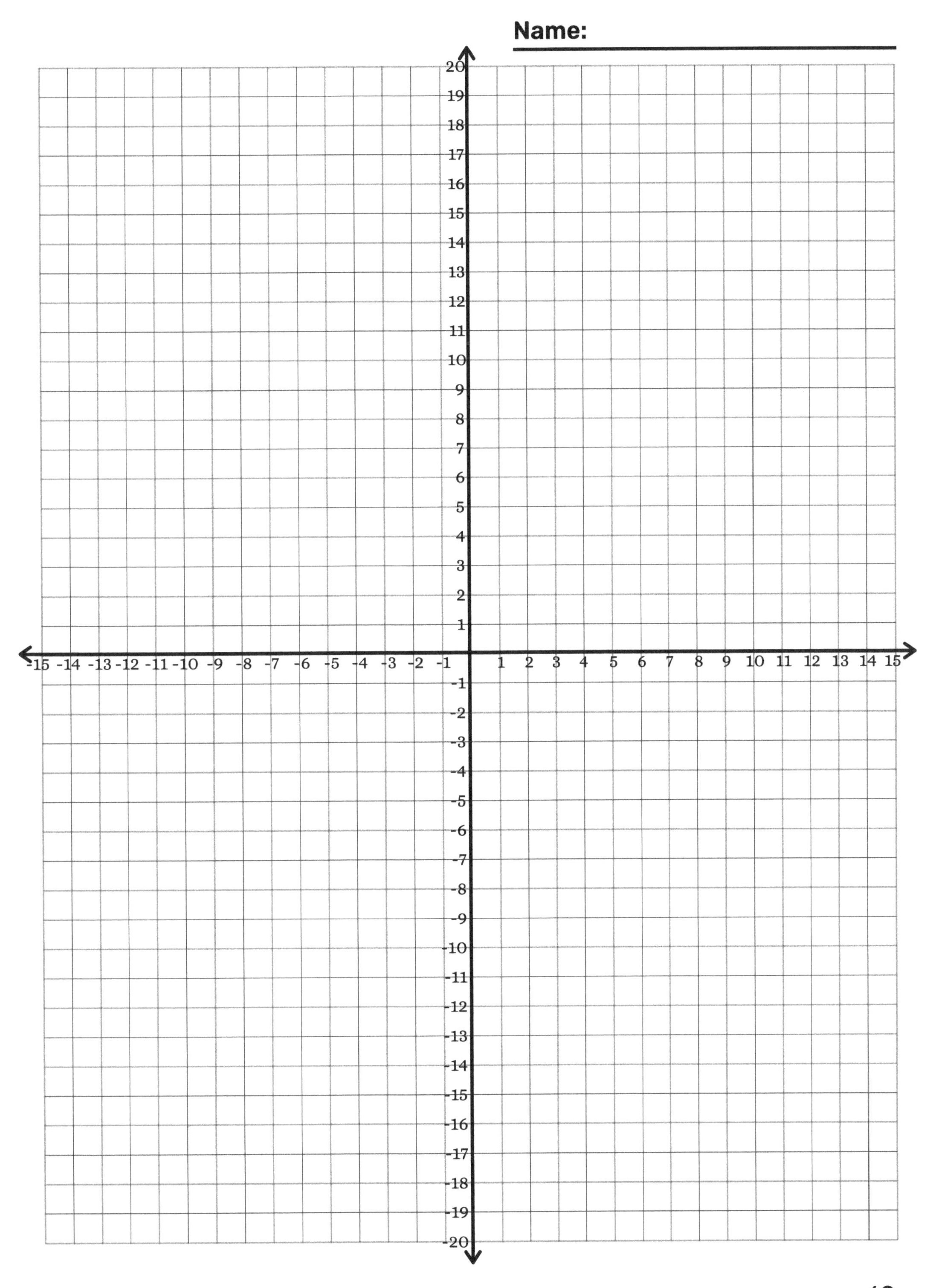

-15 -14 -13 -12 -11 -10 -9 -8 -7 -6 -5 -4 -3 -2 -1 1 2 3 4 5 6 7 8 9 10 11 12 13 14 15
20 19 18 17 16 15 14 13 12 11 10 9 8 7 6 5 4 3 2 1 -1 -2 -3 -4 -5 -6 -7 -8 -9 -10 -11 -12 -13 -14 -15 -16 -17 -18 -19 -20

FALL MYSTERY PICTURE #1 (FIRST QUADRANT)

Plot the ordered pairs, connecting with straight lines as you go. Be sure to stop when you reach **"STOP"** and begin a new series of connected lines at each **"START"**. *Have fun!*

START
(16, 28)
(17, 29)
(24, 29)
(29, 24)
(29, 11)
(24, 6)
(6, 6)
(1, 11)
(1, 24)
(6, 29)
(13, 29)
(14, 28)
STOP

START
(10, 27)
(13, 27)
(14, 28)
(14, 32)
(13, 33)
(14, 34)
(15, 34)
(16, 33)
(16, 28)
(17, 27)
(20, 27)
(18, 25)
(12, 25)
(10, 27)
STOP

START
(19, 26)
(21, 24)
(21, 9)
(18, 6)
STOP

START
(11, 26)
(9, 24)
(9, 9)
(12, 6)
STOP

START
(16, 29)
(19, 32)
(21, 32)
(23, 30)
(26, 33)
(28, 33)
STOP

START
(14, 29)
(11, 32)
(9, 32)
(7, 30)
(4, 33)
(2, 33)
STOP

START
(25, 32)
(27, 32)
(27, 30)
(25, 32)
(25, 30)
(27, 30)
STOP

START
(5, 32)
(5, 34)
(7, 34)
(5, 32)
(7, 32)
(7, 34)
STOP

Name: ____________________

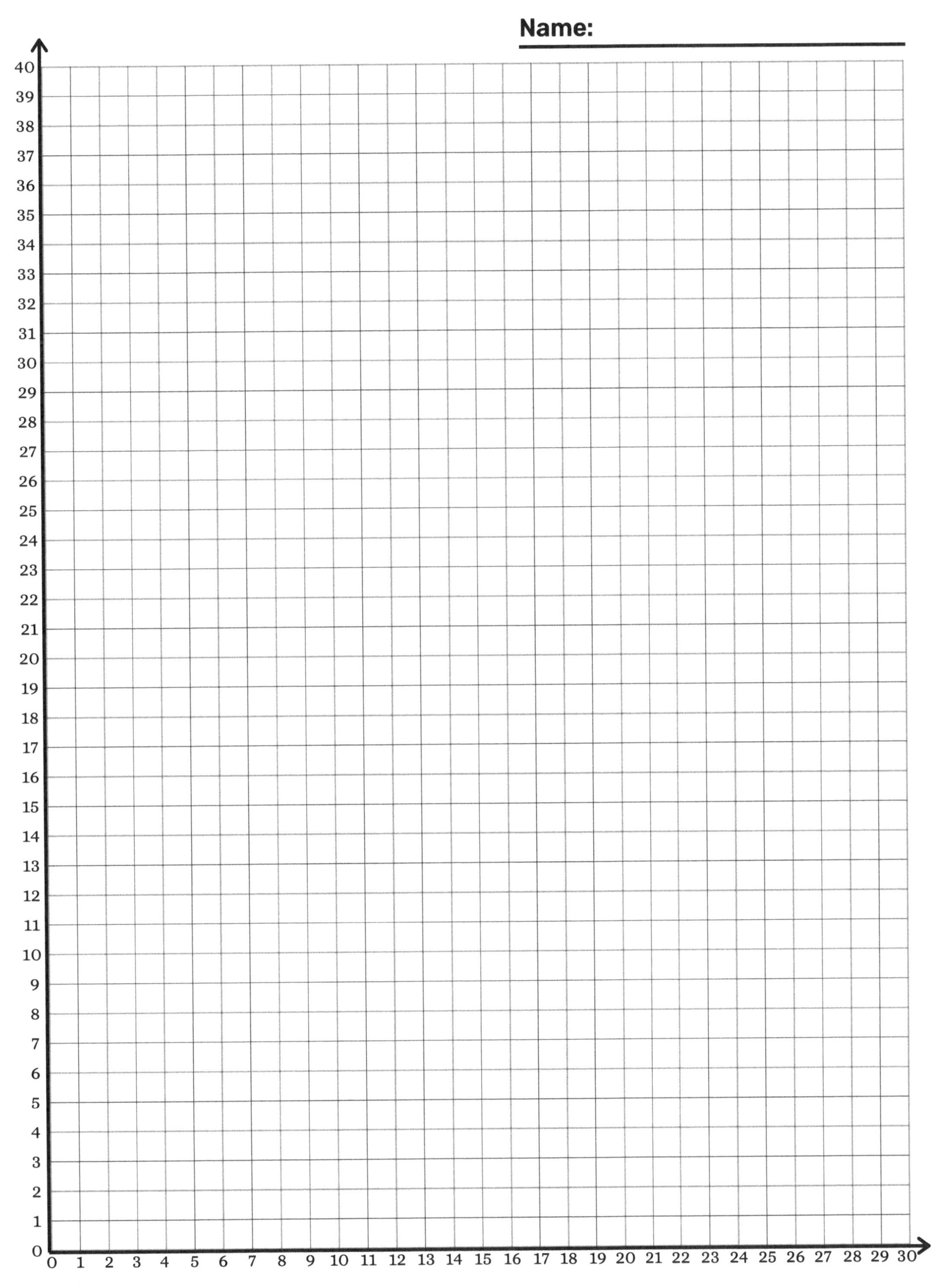
40
39
38
37
36
35
34
33
32
31
30
29
28
27
26
25
24
23
22
21
20
19
18
17
16
15
14
13
12
11
10
9
8
7
6
5
4
3
2
1
0
0 1 2 3 4 5 6 7 8 9 10 11 12 13 14 15 16 17 18 19 20 21 22 23 24 25 26 27 28 29 30

FALL MYSTERY PICTURE #1 (FOUR QUADRANT)

Plot the ordered pairs, connecting with straight lines as you go. Be sure to stop when you reach **"STOP"** and begin a new series of connected lines at each **"START"**. *Have fun!*

START
(1, 8)
(2, 9)
(9, 9)
(14, 4)
(14, -9)
(9, -14)
(-9, -14)
(-14, -9)
(-14, 4)
(-9, 9)
(-2, 9)
(-1, 8)
STOP

START
(-5, 7)
(-2, 7)
(-1, 8)
(-1, 12)
(-2, 13)
(-1, 14)
(0, 14)
(1, 13)
(1, 8)
(2, 7)
(5, 7)
(3, 5)
(-3, 5)
(-5, 7)
STOP

START
(4, 6)
(6, 4)
(6, -11)
(3, -14)
STOP

START
(-4, 6)
(-6, 4)
(-6, -11)
(-3, -14)
STOP

START
(1, 9)
(4, 12)
(6, 12)
(8, 10)
(11, 13)
(13, 13)
STOP

START
(-1, 9)
(-4, 12)
(-6, 12)
(-8, 10)
(-11, 13)
(-13, 13)
STOP

START
(10, 12)
(12, 12)
(12, 10)
(10, 12)
(10, 10)
(12, 10)
STOP

START
(-10, 12)
(-10, 14)
(-8, 14)
(-10, 12)
(-8, 12)
(-8, 14)
STOP

Name: ______________________

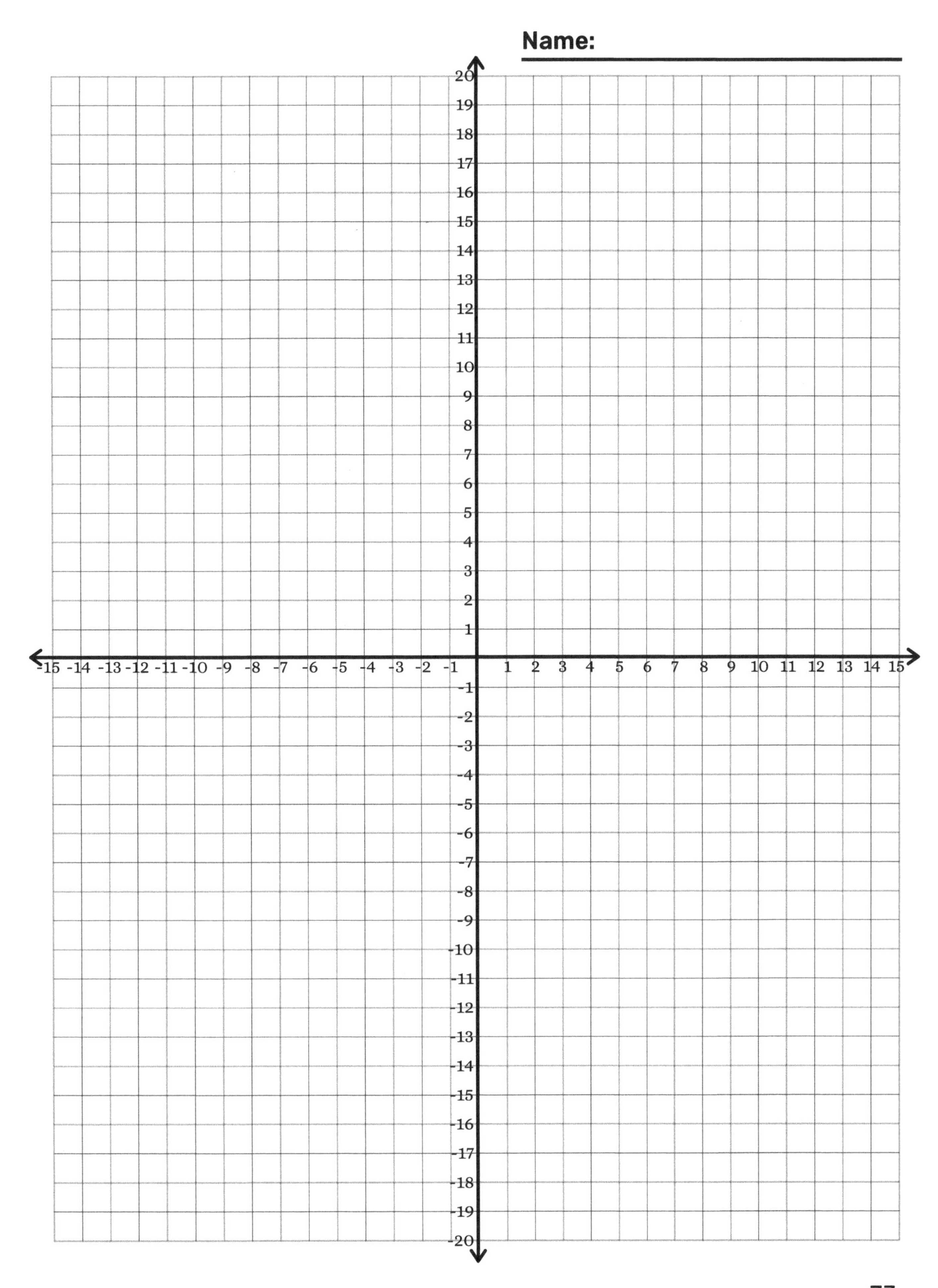

20
19
18
17
16
15
14
13
12
11
10
9
8
7
6
5
4
3
2
1
-15 -14 -13 -12 -11 -10 -9 -8 -7 -6 -5 -4 -3 -2 -1
1 2 3 4 5 6 7 8 9 10 11 12 13 14 15
-1
-2
-3
-4
-5
-6
-7
-8
-9
-10
-11
-12
-13
-14
-15
-16
-17
-18
-19
-20

FALL MYSTERY PICTURE #2
(FIRST QUADRANT)

Plot the ordered pairs, connecting with straight lines as you go. Be sure to stop when you reach **"STOP"** and begin a new series of connected lines at each **"START"**. *Have fun!*

START
(20, 30)
(29, 21)
(29, 12)
(23, 6)
(14, 6)
(5, 15)
STOP

START
(20, 30)
(20, 33)
(9, 33)
(2, 26)
(2, 15)
(5, 15)
(20, 30)
STOP

START
(4, 28)
(3, 29)
(6, 32)
(7, 31)
STOP

START
(25, 8)
(26, 8)
(27, 9)
(27, 10)
STOP

START
(14, 14)
(14, 15)
(16, 17)
(17, 17)
(18, 16)
(18, 15)
(16, 13)
(15, 13)
(12, 16)
(12, 17)
(14, 19)
(15, 19)
(17, 17)
STOP

START
(18, 18)
(18, 19)
(20, 21)
(21, 21)
(22, 20)
(22, 19)
(20, 17)
(19, 17)
(16, 20)
(16, 21)
(18, 23)
(19, 23)
(21, 21)
STOP

START
(18, 11)
(19, 10)
(21, 10)
(25, 14)
(25, 16)
(24, 17)
STOP

START
(2, 18)
(8, 18)
STOP

START
(2, 21)
(11, 21)
STOP

START
(2, 24)
(14, 24)
STOP

START
(3, 27)
(17, 27)
STOP

START
(6, 30)
(20, 30)
STOP

START
(5, 29)
(5, 15)
STOP

START
(8, 32)
(8, 18)
STOP

START
(11, 33)
(11, 21)
STOP

START
(14, 33)
(14, 24)
STOP

START
(17, 33)
(17, 27)
STOP

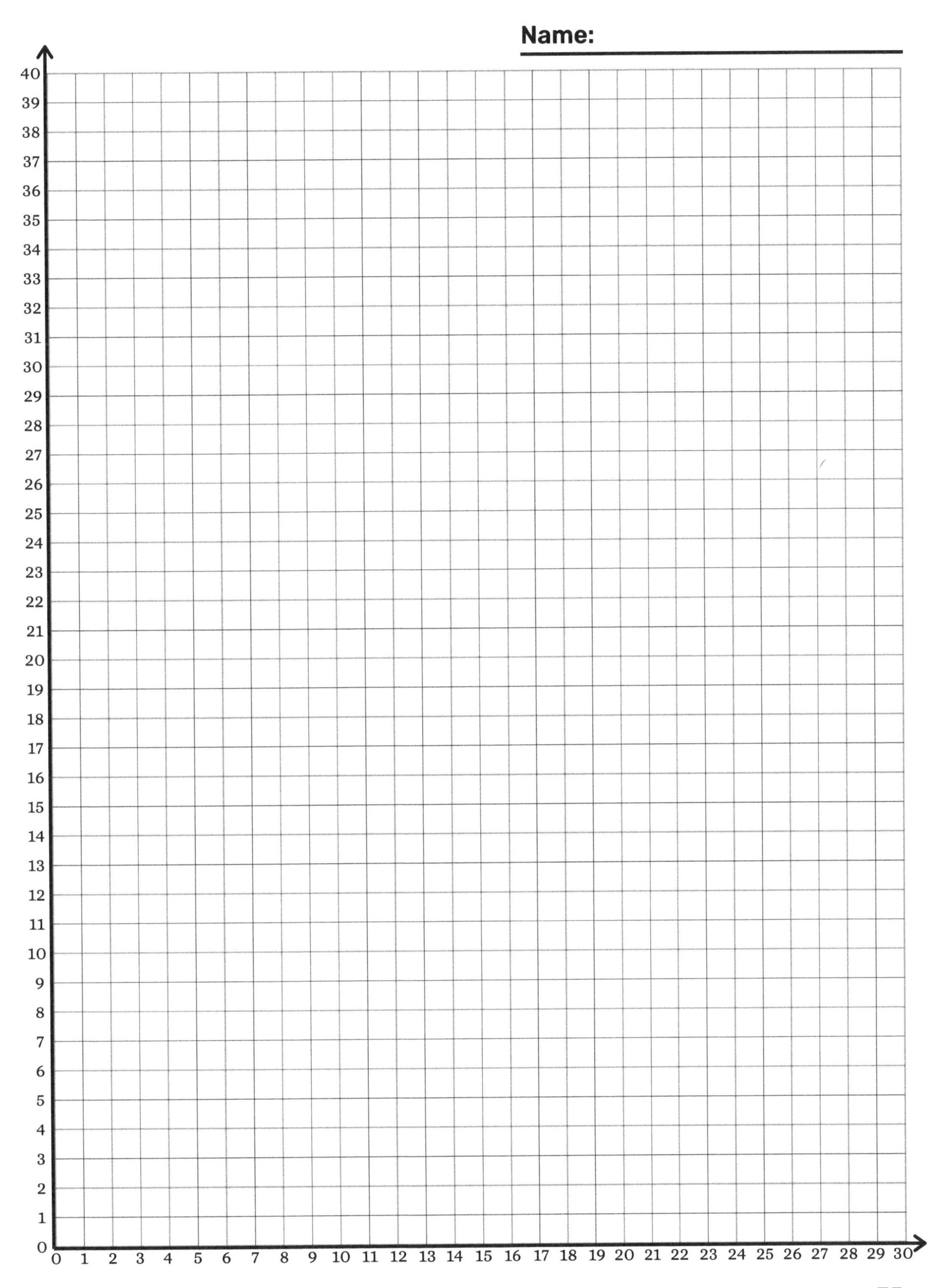
Name:
40
39
38
37
36
35
34
33
32
31
30
29
28
27
26
25
24
23
22
21
20
19
18
17
16
15
14
13
12
11
10
9
8
7
6
5
4
3
2
1
0
0 1 2 3 4 5 6 7 8 9 10 11 12 13 14 15 16 17 18 19 20 21 22 23 24 25 26 27 28 29 30

FALL MYSTERY PICTURE #2 (FOUR QUADRANT)

Plot the ordered pairs, connecting with straight lines as you go. Be sure to stop when you reach **"STOP"** and begin a new series of connected lines at each **"START"**. *Have fun!*

START
(5, 10)
(14, 1)
(14, -8)
(8, -14)
(-1, -14)
(-10, -5)
STOP

START
(5, 10)
(5, 13)
(-6, 13)
(-13, 6)
(-13, -5)
(-10, -5)
(5, 10)
STOP

START
(-11, 8)
(-12, 9)
(-9, 12)
(-8, 11)
STOP

START
(10, -12)
(11, -12)
(12, -11)
(12, -10)
STOP

START
(-1, -6)
(-1, -5)
(1, -3)
(2, -3)
(3, -4)
(3, -5)
(1, -7)
(0, -7)
(-3, -4)
(-3, -3)
(-1, -1)
(0, -1)
(2, -3)
STOP

START
(3, -2)
(3, -1)
(5, 1)
(6, 1)
(7, 0)
(7, -1)
(5, -3)
(4, -3)
(1, 0)
(1, 1)
(3, 3)
(4, 3)
(6, 1)
STOP

START
(3, -9)
(4, -10)
(6, -10)
(10, -6)
(10, -4)
(9, -3)
STOP

START
(-13, -2)
(-7, -2)
STOP

START
(-13, 1)
(-4, 1)
STOP

START
(-13, 4)
(-1, 4)
STOP

START
(-12, 7)
(2, 7)
STOP

START
(-9, 10)
(5, 10)
STOP

START
(-10, 9)
(-10, -5)
STOP

START
(-7, 12)
(-7, -2)
STOP

START
(-4, 13)
(-4, 1)
STOP

START
(-1, 13)
(-1, 4)
STOP

START
(2, 13)
(2, 7)
STOP

Name: ______________________

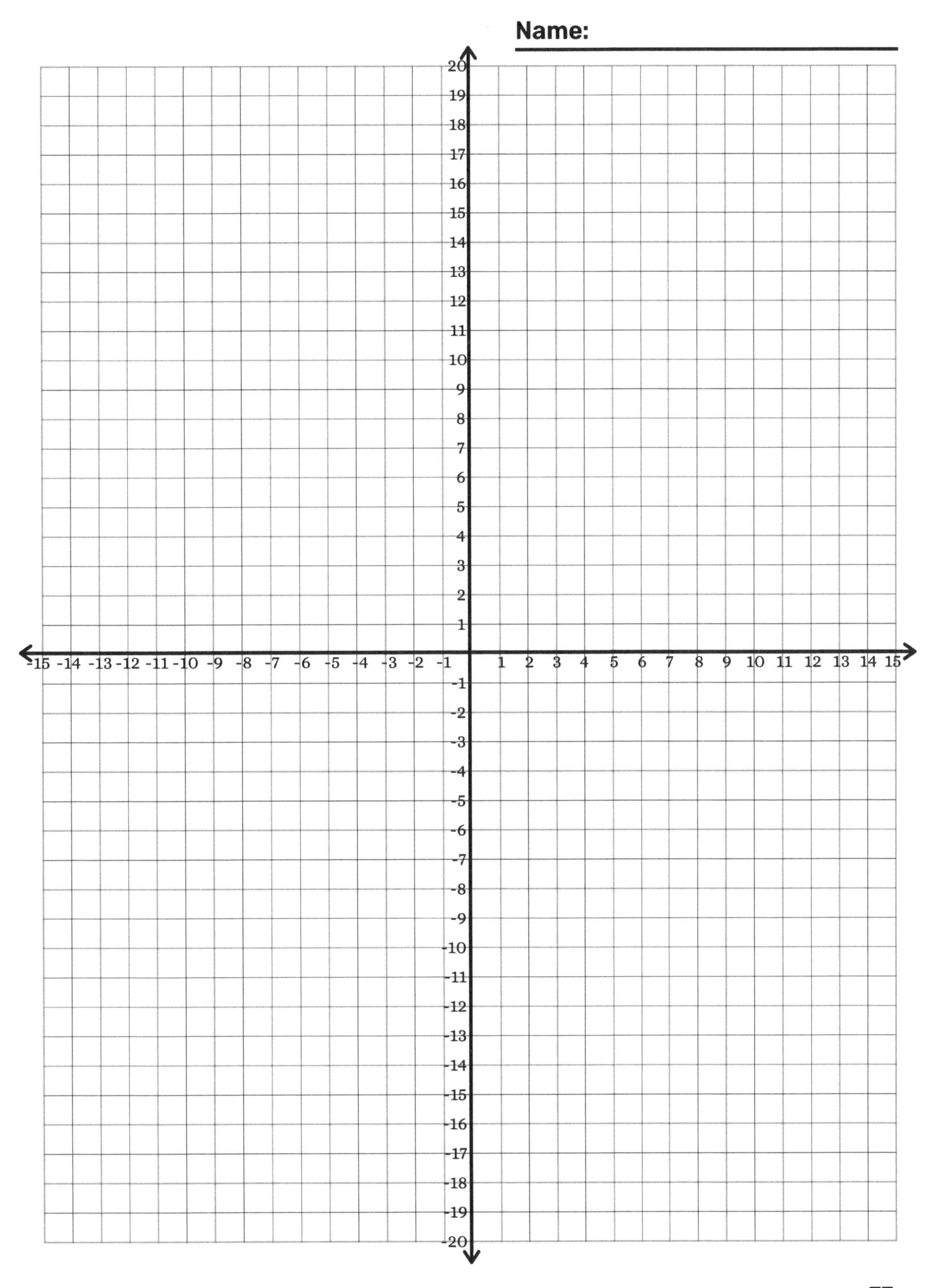

20
19
18
17
16
15
14
13
12
11
10
9
8
7
6
5
4
3
2
1
-15 -14 -13 -12 -11 -10 -9 -8 -7 -6 -5 -4 -3 -2 -1
1 2 3 4 5 6 7 8 9 10 11 12 13 14 15
-1
-2
-3
-4
-5
-6
-7
-8
-9
-10
-11
-12
-13
-14
-15
-16
-17
-18
-19
-20

FALL MYSTERY PICTURE #3 (FIRST QUADRANT)

Plot the ordered pairs, connecting with straight lines as you go. Be sure to stop when you reach **"STOP"** and begin a new series of connected lines at each **"START"**. *Have fun!*

START
(23, 25)
(25, 23)
(25, 9)
(21, 5)
(15, 5)
(14, 6)
(13, 5)
(7, 5)
(3, 9)
(3, 23)
(6, 26)
(12, 26)
(13, 25)
(13, 24)
(12, 24)
(14, 24)
(16, 26)
(20, 26)
STOP

START
(15, 25)
(15, 28)
(16, 29)
(16, 30)
(14, 30)
(13, 29)
(13, 25)
STOP

START
(10, 32)
(13, 29)
(13, 31)
(11, 33)
(9, 33)
(9, 31)
(11, 29)
(13, 29)
STOP

START
(20, 23)
(19, 23)
(18, 22)
(18, 19)
(19, 18)
(21, 18)
(23, 20)
(23, 28)
(24, 28)
(25, 29)
(25, 31)
(24, 32)
(24, 33)
(23, 34)
(20, 34)
(19, 33)
(19, 32)
(18, 31)
(18, 29)
(19, 28)
(20, 28)
(20, 23)
(19, 22)
(18, 22)
STOP

START
(19, 31)
(20, 32)
(21, 31)
(19, 31)
(19, 33)
(21, 33)
(21, 31)
STOP

START
(22, 31)
(23, 32)
(24, 31)
(22, 31)
(22, 33)
(24, 33)
(24, 31)
STOP

START
(19, 30)
(20, 29)
(23, 29)
(24, 30)
STOP

START
(20, 19)
(21, 18)
STOP

START
(21, 20)
(22, 19)
STOP

START
(22, 21)
(23, 20)
STOP

START
(21, 32)
(22, 32)
STOP

Name: ____________________

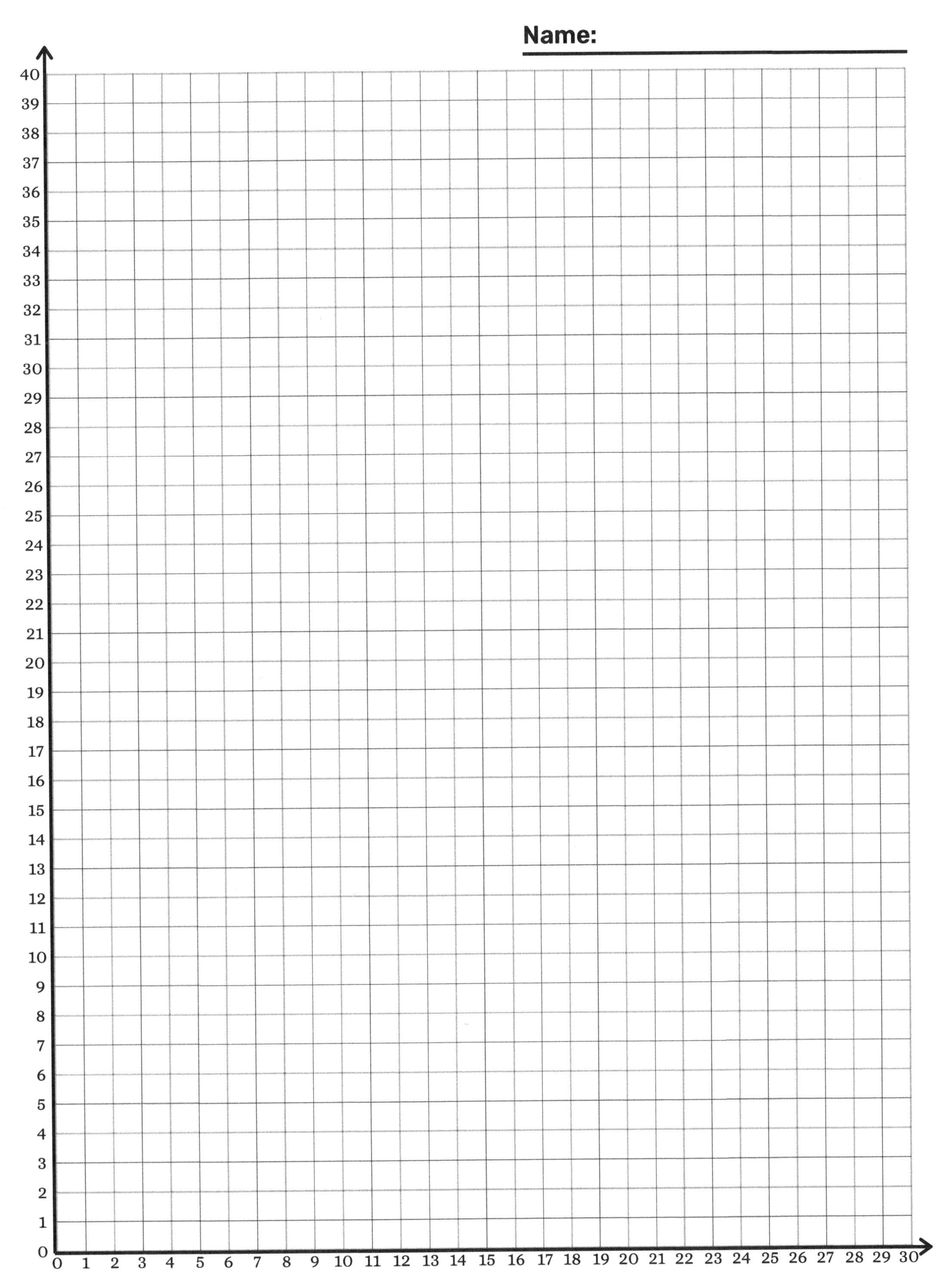

40
39
38
37
36
35
34
33
32
31
30
29
28
27
26
25
24
23
22
21
20
19
18
17
16
15
14
13
12
11
10
9
8
7
6
5
4
3
2
1
0
0 1 2 3 4 5 6 7 8 9 10 11 12 13 14 15 16 17 18 19 20 21 22 23 24 25 26 27 28 29 30

FALL MYSTERY PICTURE #3
(FOUR QUADRANT)

Plot the ordered pairs, connecting with straight lines as you go. Be sure to stop when you reach **"STOP"** and begin a new series of connected lines at each **"START"**. *Have fun!*

START
(8, 5)
(10, 3)
(10, -11)
(6, -15)
(0, -15)
(-1, -14)
(-2, -15)
(-8, -15)
(-12, -11)
(-12, 3)
(-9, 6)
(-3, 6)
(-2, 5)
(-2, 4)
(-3, 4)
(-1, 4)
(1, 6)
(5, 6)
STOP

START
(0, 5)
(0, 8)
(1, 9)
(1, 10)
(-1, 10)
(-2, 9)
(-2, 5)
STOP

START
(-5, 12)
(-2, 9)
(-2, 11)
(-4, 13)
(-6, 13)
(-6, 11)
(-4, 9)
(-2, 9)
STOP

START
(5, 3)
(4, 3)
(3, 2)
(3, -1)
(4, -2)
(6, -2)
(8, 0)
(8, 8)
(9, 8)
(10, 9)
(10, 11)
(9, 12)
(9, 13)
(8, 14)
(5, 14)
(4, 13)
(4, 12)
(3, 11)
(3, 9)
(4, 8)
(5, 8)
(5, 3)
(4, 2)
(3, 2)
STOP

START
(4, 11)
(5, 12)
(6, 11)
(4, 11)
(4, 13)
(6, 13)
(6, 11)
STOP

START
(7, 11)
(8, 12)
(9, 11)
(7, 11)
(7, 13)
(9, 13)
(9, 11)
STOP

START
(4, 10)
(5, 9)
(8, 9)
(9, 10)
STOP

START
(5, -1)
(6, -2)
STOP

START
(6, 0)
(7, -1)
STOP

START
(7, 1)
(8, 0)
STOP

START
(6, 12)
(7, 12)
STOP

Name: ____________________

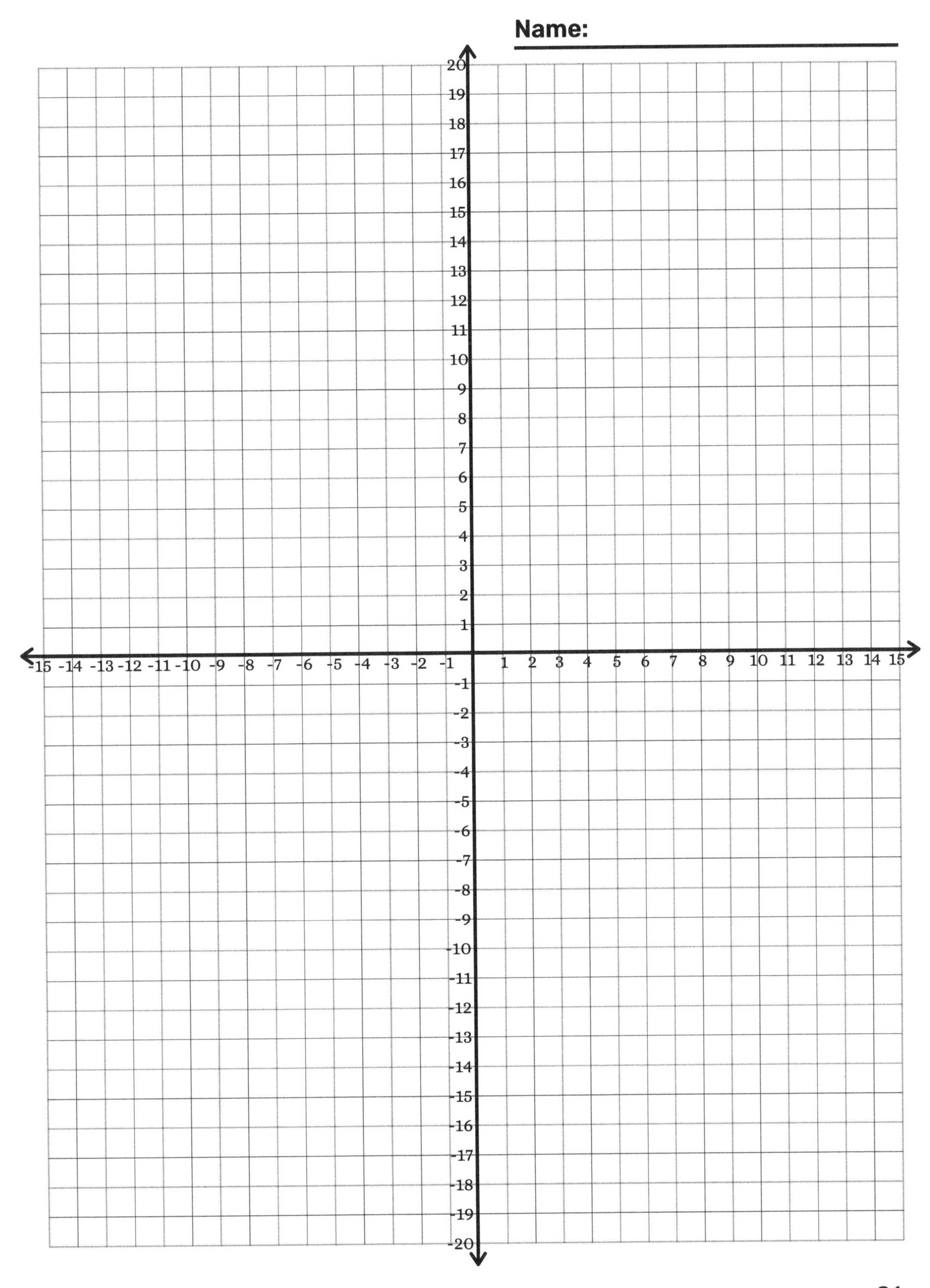
20
19
18
17
16
15
14
13
12
11
10
9
8
7
6
5
4
3
2
1
-15 -14 -13 -12 -11 -10 -9 -8 -7 -6 -5 -4 -3 -2 -1
1 2 3 4 5 6 7 8 9 10 11 12 13 14 15
-1
-2
-3
-4
-5
-6
-7
-8
-9
-10
-11
-12
-13
-14
-15
-16
-17
-18
-19
-20

FALL MYSTERY PICTURE #4 (FIRST QUADRANT)

Plot the ordered pairs, connecting with straight lines as you go. Be sure to stop when you reach **"STOP"** and begin a new series of connected lines at each **"START"**. *Have fun!*

START
(12, 26)
(12, 25)
(10, 23)
(6, 23)
(4, 25)
(5, 25)
(5, 24)
(4, 25)
(4, 27)
(8, 31)
(10, 31)
(10, 30)
(10, 31)
(11, 32)
(12, 31)
(12, 30)
(12, 31)
(14, 29)
(14, 25)
(13, 24)
(18, 19)
(18, 10)
(16, 8)
(4, 8)
(4, 9)
(5, 10)
(9, 10)
(8, 10)
(6, 12)
(6, 16)
(8, 18)
(6, 18)
(4, 20)
(4, 23)
(5, 23)
(7, 21)
(7, 22)
(8, 23)
STOP

START
(13, 17)
(12, 18)
(7, 18)
(5, 16)
(5, 12)
(7, 10)
(4, 10)
(3, 9)
(3, 8)
(4, 8)
STOP

START
(18, 10)
(22, 10)
(25, 13)
(25, 24)
(25, 23)
(29, 23)
(29, 26)
(27, 28)
(22, 28)
(20, 26)
(20, 18)
(18, 16)
STOP

START
(9, 27)
(9, 28)
(8, 28)
(8, 27)
(10, 27)
(10, 29)
(8, 29)
(8, 28)
STOP

START
(2, 22)
(4, 22)
(4, 24)
(2, 22)
(2, 24)
(4, 24)
STOP

START
(12, 22)
(9, 22)
(7, 20)
(5, 22)
(4, 22)
STOP

Name: ____________________

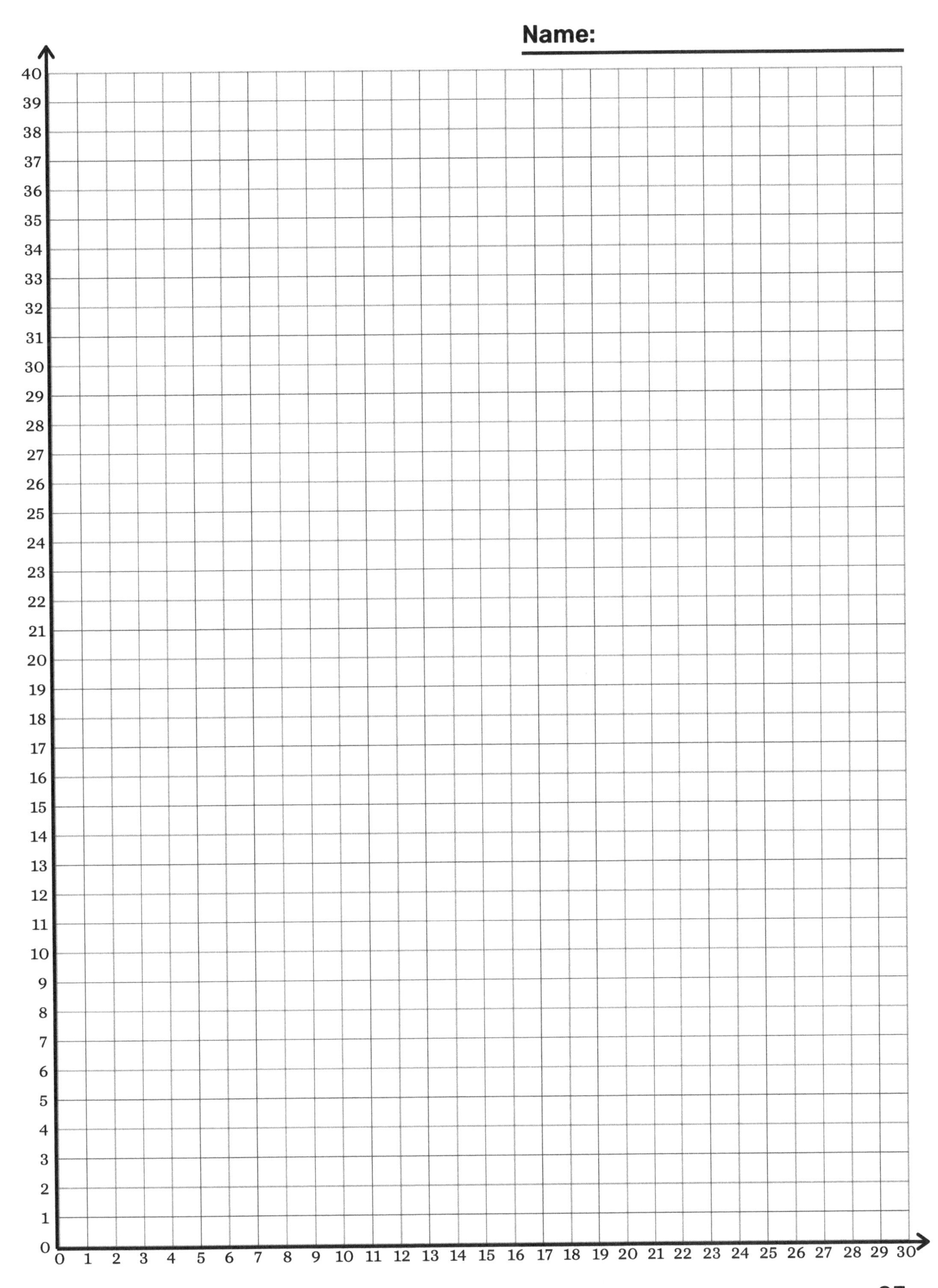

40
39
38
37
36
35
34
33
32
31
30
29
28
27
26
25
24
23
22
21
20
19
18
17
16
15
14
13
12
11
10
9
8
7
6
5
4
3
2
1
0
0 1 2 3 4 5 6 7 8 9 10 11 12 13 14 15 16 17 18 19 20 21 22 23 24 25 26 27 28 29 30

FALL MYSTERY PICTURE #4 (FOUR QUADRANT)

Plot the ordered pairs, connecting with straight lines as you go. Be sure to stop when you reach **"STOP"** and begin a new series of connected lines at each **"START"**. *Have fun!*

START (-3, 6) (-3, 5) (-5, 3) (-9, 3) (-11, 5) (-10, 5) (-10, 4) (-11, 5) (-11, 7) (-7, 11) (-5, 11) (-5, 10) (-5, 11) (-4, 12) (-3, 11) (-3, 10) (-3, 11) (-1, 9) (-1, 5) (-2, 4) (3, -1) (3, -10) (1, -12) (-11, -12) (-11, -11) (-10, -10) (-6, -10) (-7, -10) (-9, -8) (-9, -4) (-7, -2) (-9, -2) (-11, 0) (-11, 3) (-10, 3) (-8, 1) (-8, 2) (-7, 3) **STOP**	**START** (-2, -3) (-3, -2) (-8, -2) (-10, -4) (-10, -8) (-8, -10) (-11, -10) (-12, -11) (-12, -12) (-11, -12) **STOP** **START** (3, -10) (7, -10) (10, -7) (10, 4) (10, 3) (14, 3) (14, 6) (12, 8) (7, 8) (5, 6) (5, -2) (3, -4) **STOP** **START** (-6, 7) (-6, 8) (-7, 8) (-7, 7) (-5, 7) (-5, 9) (-7, 9) (-7, 8) **STOP**	**START** (-13, 2) (-11, 2) (-11, 4) (-13, 2) (-13, 4) (-11, 4) **STOP** **START** (-3, 2) (-6, 2) (-8, 0) (-10, 2) (-11, 2) **STOP**

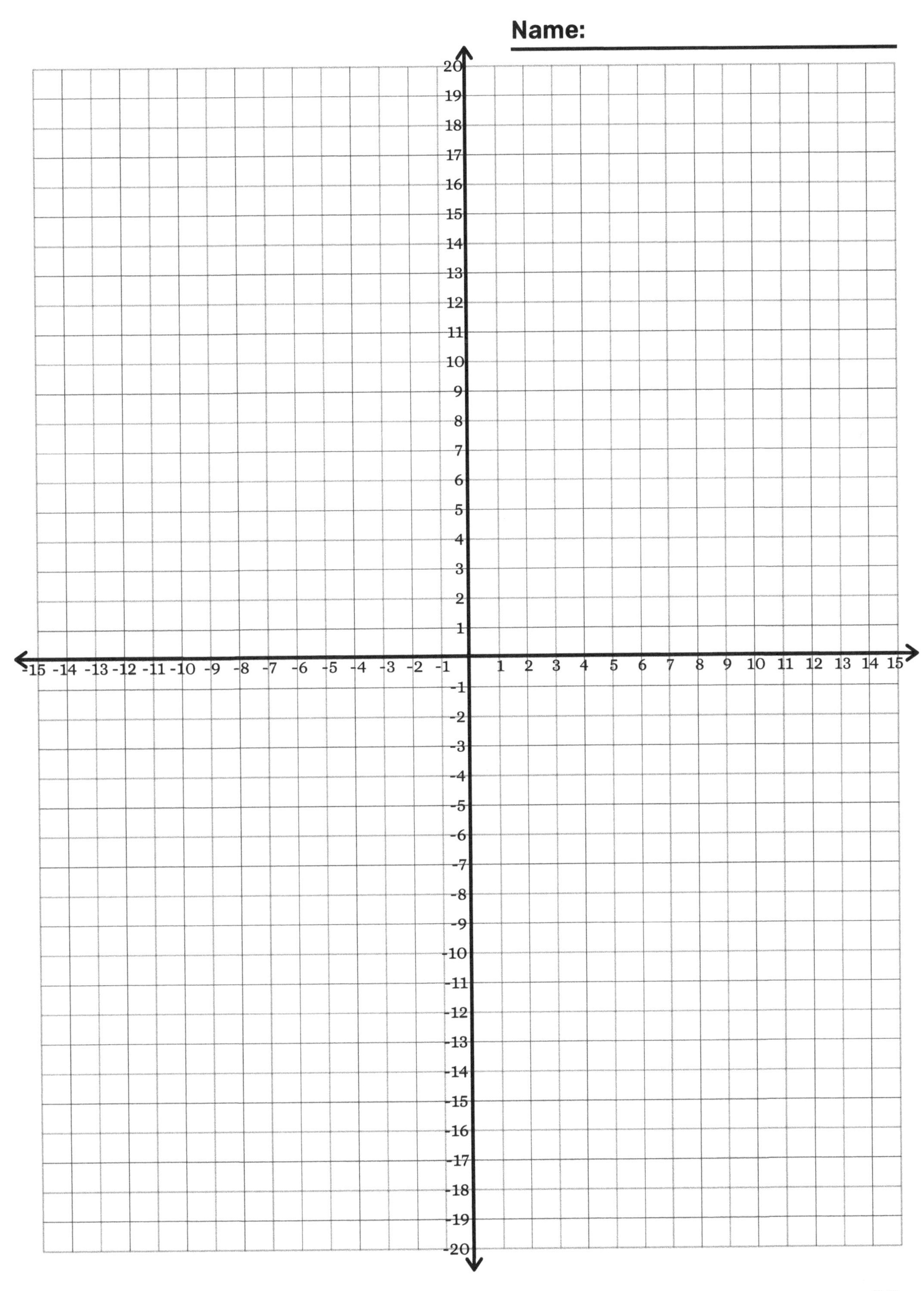
Name:
20 19 18 17 16 15 14 13 12 11 10 9 8 7 6 5 4 3 2 1
-15 -14 -13 -12 -11 -10 -9 -8 -7 -6 -5 -4 -3 -2 -1
1 2 3 4 5 6 7 8 9 10 11 12 13 14 15
-1 -2 -3 -4 -5 -6 -7 -8 -9 -10 -11 -12 -13 -14 -15 -16 -17 -18 -19 -20

HALLOWEEN MYSTERY PICTURE #1 (FIRST QUADRANT)

Plot the ordered pairs, connecting with straight lines as you go. Be sure to stop when you reach **"STOP"** and begin a new series of connected lines at each **"START"**. *Have fun!*

START
(16, 40)
(16, 27)
(11, 22)
(9, 22)
(9, 21)
(11, 21)
(7, 17)
(7, 10)
(11, 6)
(21, 6)
(25, 10)
(25, 17)
(21, 21)
(23, 21)
(23, 22)
(21, 22)
(16, 27)
STOP

START
(11, 21)
(21, 21)
STOP

START
(11, 22)
(21, 22)
STOP

START
(12, 23)
(20, 23)
STOP

START
(15, 23)
(15, 22)
STOP

START
(17, 23)
(17, 22)
STOP

START
(9, 19)
(8, 20)
(4, 20)
(2, 18)
STOP

START
(7, 17)
(6, 18)
(4, 18)
(2, 16)
STOP

START
(7, 15)
(5, 15)
(2, 12)
STOP

START
(7, 12)
(5, 12)
(2, 9)
STOP

START
(23, 19)
(24, 20)
(28, 20)
(30, 18)
STOP

START
(25, 17)
(26, 18)
(28, 18)
(30, 16)
STOP

START
(25, 15)
(27, 15)
(30, 12)
STOP

START
(25, 12)
(27, 12)
(30, 9)
STOP

START
(11, 11)
(12, 11)
(12, 13)
(10, 13)
(10, 11)
(11, 11)
(13, 9)
(19, 9)
(21, 11)
(22, 11)
(22, 13)
(20, 13)
(20, 11)
(21, 11)
STOP

START
(16, 18)
(15, 19)
(13, 19)
(12, 18)
(12, 16)
(13, 15)
(15, 15)
(16, 16)
(16, 18)
(17, 19)
(19, 19)
(20, 18)
(20, 16)
(19, 15)
(17, 15)
(16, 16)
STOP

START
(13, 18)
(15, 18)
(15, 16)
(13, 16)
(13, 18)
STOP

START
(17, 18)
(19, 18)
(19, 16)
(17, 16)
(17, 18)
STOP

Name: ______________________

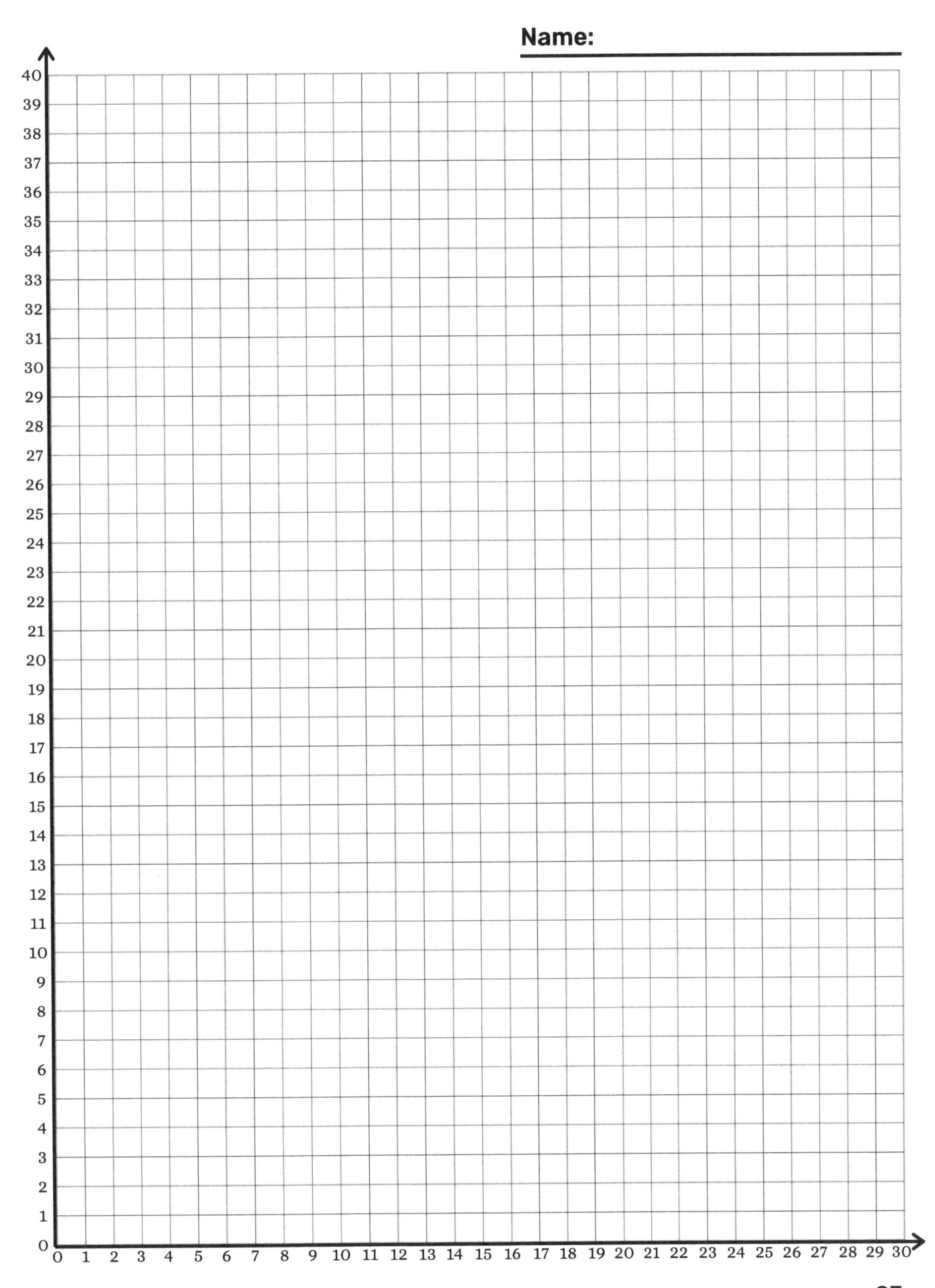

40
39
38
37
36
35
34
33
32
31
30
29
28
27
26
25
24
23
22
21
20
19
18
17
16
15
14
13
12
11
10
9
8
7
6
5
4
3
2
1
0
0 1 2 3 4 5 6 7 8 9 10 11 12 13 14 15 16 17 18 19 20 21 22 23 24 25 26 27 28 29 30

HALLOWEEN MYSTERY PICTURE #1 (FOUR QUADRANT)

Plot the ordered pairs, connecting with straight lines as you go. Be sure to stop when you reach **"STOP"** and begin a new series of connected lines at each **"START"**. *Have fun!*

START
(1, 20)
(1, 7)
(-4, 2)
(-6, 2)
(-6, 1)
(-4, 1)
(-8, -3)
(-8, -10)
(-4, -14)
(6, -14)
(10, -10)
(10, -3)
(6, 1)
(8, 1)
(8, 2)
(6, 2)
(1, 7)
STOP

START
(-4, 1)
(6, 1)
STOP

START
(-4, 2)
(6, 2)
STOP

START
(-3, 3)
(5, 3)
STOP

START
(0, 3)
(0, 2)
STOP

START
(2, 3)
(2, 2)
STOP

START
(-6, -1)
(-7, 0)
(-11, 0)
(-13, -2)
STOP

START
(-8, -3)
(-9, -2)
(-11, -2)
(-13, -4)
STOP

START
(-8, -5)
(-10, -5)
(-13, -8)
STOP

START
(-8, -8)
(-10, -8)
(-13, -11)
STOP

START
(8, -1)
(9, 0)
(13, 0)
(15, -2)
STOP

START
(10, -3)
(11, -2)
(13, -2)
(15, -4)
STOP

START
(10, -5)
(12, -5)
(15, -8)
STOP

START
(10, -8)
(12, -8)
(15, -11)
STOP

START
(-4, -9)
(-3, -9)
(-3, -7)
(-5, -7)
(-5, -9)
(-4, -9)
(-2, -11)
(4, -11)
(6, -9)
(7, -9)
(7, -7)
(5, -7)
(5, -9)
(6, -9)
STOP

START
(1, -2)
(0, -1)
(-2, -1)
(-3, -2)
(-3, -4)
(-2, -5)
(0, -5)
(1, -4)
(1, -2)
(2, -1)
(4, -1)
(5, -2)
(5, -4)
(4, -5)
(2, -5)
(1, -4)
STOP

START
(-2, -2)
(0, -2)
(0, -4)
(-2, -4)
(-2, -2)
STOP

START
(2, -2)
(4, -2)
(4, -4)
(2, -4)
(2, -2)
STOP

Name: ____________________

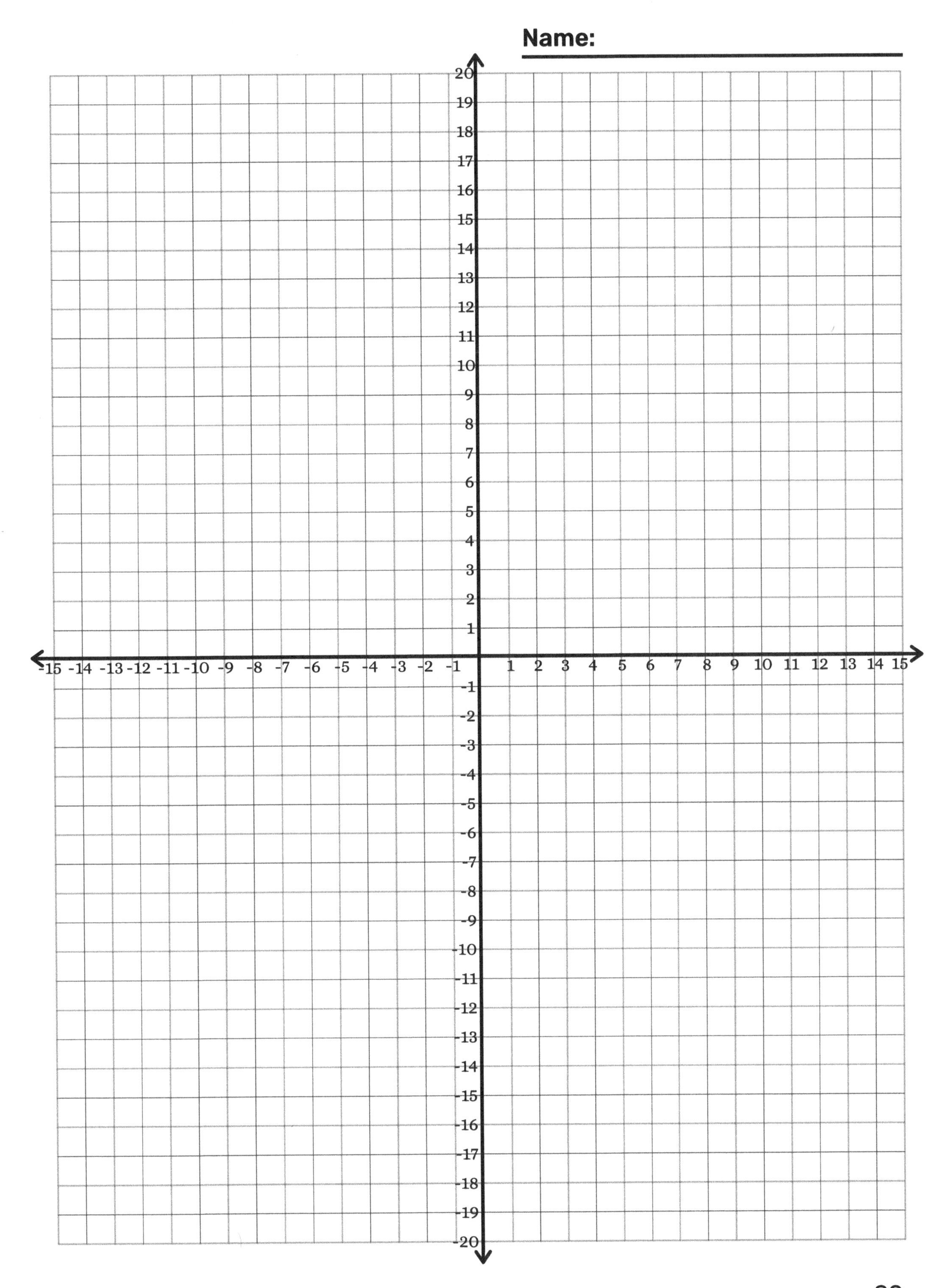

20
19
18
17
16
15
14
13
12
11
10
9
8
7
6
5
4
3
2
1
-15 -14 -13 -12 -11 -10 -9 -8 -7 -6 -5 -4 -3 -2 -1
1 2 3 4 5 6 7 8 9 10 11 12 13 14 15
-1
-2
-3
-4
-5
-6
-7
-8
-9
-10
-11
-12
-13
-14
-15
-16
-17
-18
-19
-20

HALLOWEEN MYSTERY PICTURE #2 (FIRST QUADRANT)

Plot the ordered pairs, connecting with straight lines as you go. Be sure to stop when you reach **"STOP"** and begin a new series of connected lines at each **"START"**. *Have fun!*

START
(4, 4)
(4, 34)
(26, 34)
(26, 4)
(4, 4)
STOP

START
(4, 7)
(2, 7)
(2, 6)
(0, 6)
(0, 10)
(2, 10)
(2, 7)
(2, 9)
(4, 9)
STOP

START
(26, 7)
(28, 7)
(28, 6)
(30, 6)
(30, 10)
(28, 10)
(28, 7)
(28, 9)
(26, 9)
STOP

START
(4, 18)
(3, 18)
(2, 19)
(2, 22)
(3, 23)
(4, 23)
STOP

START
(26, 18)
(27, 18)
(28, 19)
(28, 22)
(27, 23)
(26, 23)
STOP

START
(4, 22)
(5, 23)
(5, 28)
(7, 26)
(9, 28)
(11, 26)
(13, 28)
(15, 26)
(17, 28)
(19, 26)
(21, 28)
(23, 26)
(25, 28)
(25, 23)
(26, 22)
STOP

START
(7, 23)
(7, 25)
(14, 25)
(14, 23)
(7, 23)
STOP

START
(16, 23)
(16, 25)
(23, 25)
(23, 23)
(16, 23)
STOP

START
(7, 17)
(7, 20)
(9, 22)
(12, 22)
(14, 20)
(14, 17)
(12, 15)
(9, 15)
(7, 17)
STOP

START
(16, 17)
(16, 20)
(18, 22)
(21, 22)
(23, 20)
(23, 17)
(21, 15)
(18, 15)
(16, 17)
STOP

START
(9, 17)
(9, 20)
(12, 20)
(12, 17)
(9, 17)
STOP

START
(18, 17)
(18, 20)
(21, 20)
(21, 17)
(18, 17)
STOP

START
(10, 12)
(20, 12)
(20, 9)
(18, 7)
(12, 7)
(10, 9)
(10, 12)
STOP

START
(11, 12)
(12, 11)
(13, 12)
(14, 11)
(15, 12)
(16, 11)
(17, 12)
(18, 11)
(19, 12)
STOP

START
(13, 7)
(14, 8)
(15, 7)
(16, 8)
(17, 7)
STOP

START
(6, 9)
(9, 6)
STOP

START
(6, 8)
(7, 9)
STOP

START
(7, 7)
(8, 8)
STOP

START
(8, 6)
(9, 7)
STOP

START
(22, 12)
(25, 15)
STOP

START
(22, 13)
(23, 12)
STOP

START
(23, 14)
(24, 13)
STOP

START
(24, 15)
(25, 14)
STOP

Name: ____________________

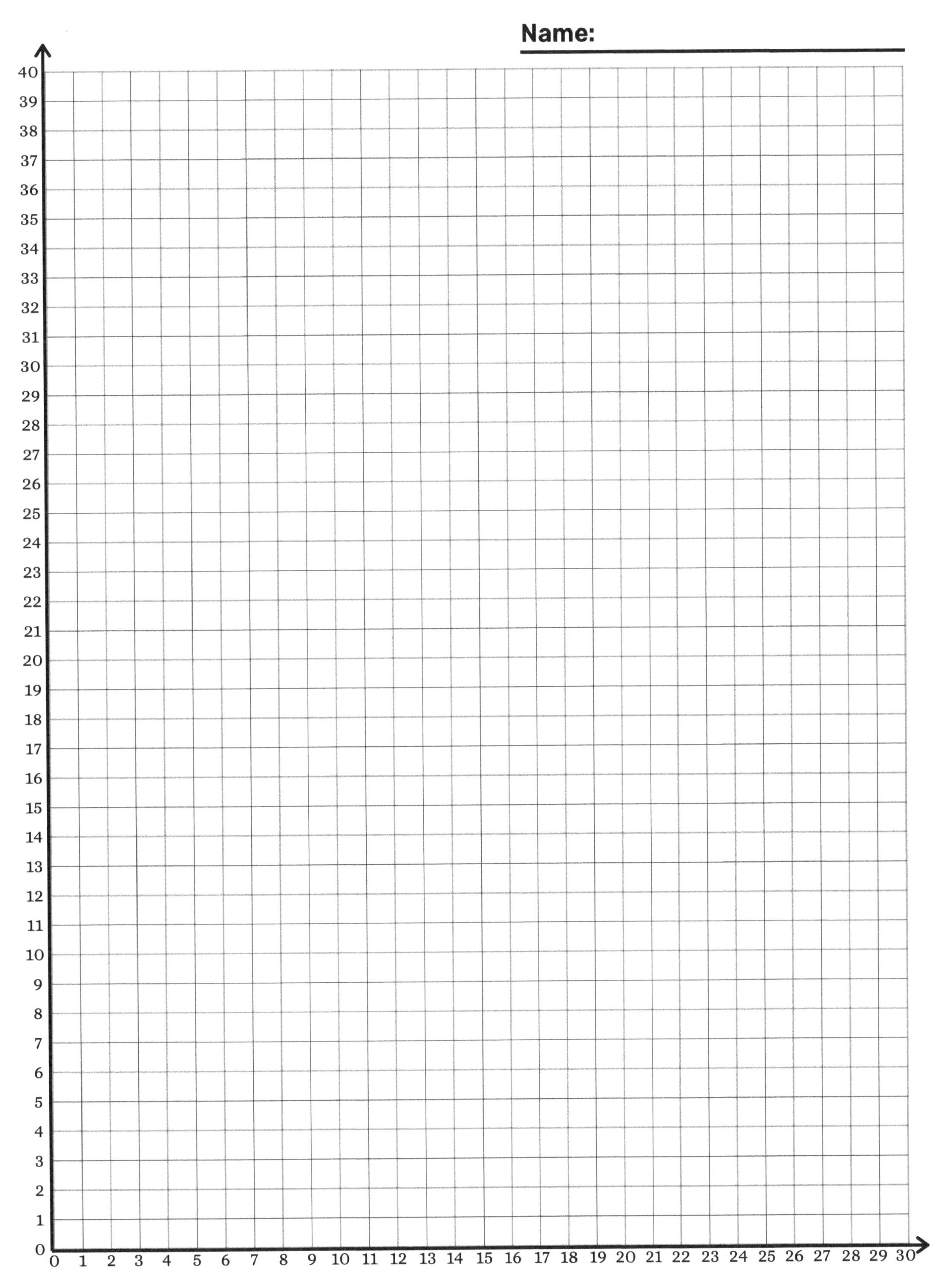

40
39
38
37
36
35
34
33
32
31
30
29
28
27
26
25
24
23
22
21
20
19
18
17
16
15
14
13
12
11
10
9
8
7
6
5
4
3
2
1
0
0 1 2 3 4 5 6 7 8 9 10 11 12 13 14 15 16 17 18 19 20 21 22 23 24 25 26 27 28 29 30

HALLOWEEN MYSTERY PICTURE #2 (FOUR QUADRANT)

Plot the ordered pairs, connecting with straight lines as you go. Be sure to stop when you reach **"STOP"** and begin a new series of connected lines at each **"START"**. *Have fun!*

START
(-11, -16)
(-11, 14)
(11, 14)
(11, -16)
(-11, -16)
STOP

START
(-11, -13)
(-13, -13)
(-13, -14)
(-15, -14)
(-15, -10)
(-13, -10)
(-13, -13)
(-13, -11)
(-11, -11)
STOP

START
(11, -13)
(13, -13)
(13, -14)
(15, -14)
(15, -10)
(13, -10)
(13, -13)
(13, -11)
(11, -11)
STOP

START
(-11, -2)
(-12, -2)
(-13, -1)
(-13, 2)
(-12, 3)
(-11, 3)
STOP

START
(11, -2)
(12, -2)
(13, -1)
(13, 2)
(12, 3)
(11, 3)
STOP

START
(-11, 2)
(-10, 3)
(-10, 8)
(-8, 6)
(-6, 8)
(-4, 6)
(-2, 8)
(0, 6)
(2, 8)
(4, 6)
(6, 8)
(8, 6)
(10, 8)
(10, 3)
(11, 2)
STOP

START
(-8, 3)
(-8, 5)
(-1, 5)
(-1, 3)
(-8. 3)
STOP

START
(1, 3)
(1, 5)
(8, 5)
(8, 3)
(1, 3)
STOP

START
(-8, -3)
(-8, 0)
(-5, 2)
(-3, 2)
(-1, 0)
(-1, -3)
(-3, -5)
(-6, -5)
(-8, -3)
STOP

START
(1, -3)
(1, 0)
(3, 2)
(6, 2)
(8, 0)
(8, -3)
(6, -5)
(3, -5)
(1, -3)
STOP

START
(-6, -3)
(-6, 0)
(-3, 0)
(-3, -3)
(-6, -3)
STOP

START
(3, -3)
(3, 0)
(6, 0)
(6, -3)
(3, -3)
STOP

START
(-5, -8)
(5, -8)
(5, -11)
(3, -13)
(-3, -13)
(-5, -11)
(-5, -8)
STOP

START
(-4, -8)
(-3, -9)
(-2, -8)
(-1, -9)
(0, -8)
(1, -9)
(2, -8)
(3, -9)
(4, -8)
STOP

START
(-2, -13)
(-1, -12)
(0, -13)
(1, -12)
(2, -13)
STOP

START
(-9, -11)
(-6, -14)
STOP

START
(-9, -12)
(-8, -11)
STOP

START
(-8, -13)
(-7, -12)
STOP

START
(-7, -14)
(-6, -13)
STOP

START
(7, -8)
(10, -5)
STOP

START
(7, -7)
(8, -8)
STOP

START
(8, -6)
(9, -7)
STOP

START
(9, -5)
(10, -6)
STOP

Name: ______________________

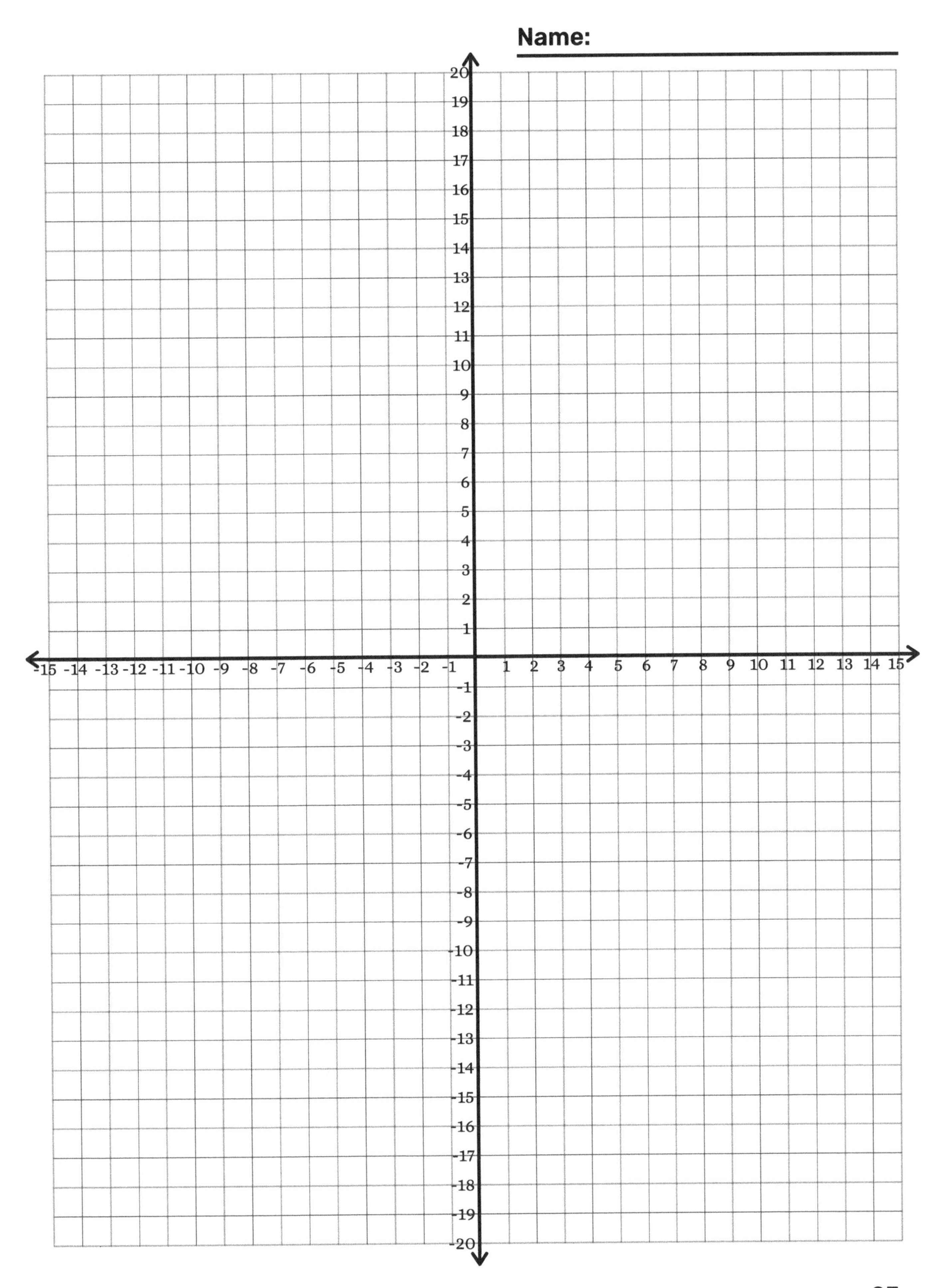

20
19
18
17
16
15
14
13
12
11
10
9
8
7
6
5
4
3
2
1
-15 -14 -13 -12 -11 -10 -9 -8 -7 -6 -5 -4 -3 -2 -1
1 2 3 4 5 6 7 8 9 10 11 12 13 14 15
-1
-2
-3
-4
-5
-6
-7
-8
-9
-10
-11
-12
-13
-14
-15
-16
-17
-18
-19
-20

THANKSGIVING MYSTERY PICTURE #1 (FIRST QUADRANT)

Plot the ordered pairs, connecting with straight lines as you go. Be sure to stop when you reach **"STOP"** and begin a new series of connected lines at each **"START"**. *Have fun!*

START
(25, 19)
(29, 15)
(29, 9)
(3, 9)
(3, 18)
(2, 18)
(2, 19)
(9, 26)
(14, 26)
(13, 25)
(11, 25)
(4, 18)
(4, 10)
(29, 10)
STOP

START
(4, 15)
(29, 15)
STOP

START
(21, 23)
(18, 26)
(16, 26)
(17, 25)
(19, 25)
STOP

START
(23, 21)
(24, 20)
STOP

START
(15, 27)
(13, 25)
(13, 24)
(12, 23)
(12, 22)
(11, 21)
(11, 20)
(12, 19)
(18, 19)
(19, 20)
(19, 21)
(18, 22)
(18, 23)
(17, 24)
(17, 25)
(15, 27)
STOP

START
(22, 35)
(22, 24)
(20, 22)
(20, 18)
(21, 18)
(21, 21)
(22, 21)
(22, 18)
(23, 18)
(23, 21)
(24, 21)
(24, 18)
(25, 18)
(25, 22)
(23, 24)
(23, 35)
(22, 35)
STOP

Name: ____________________

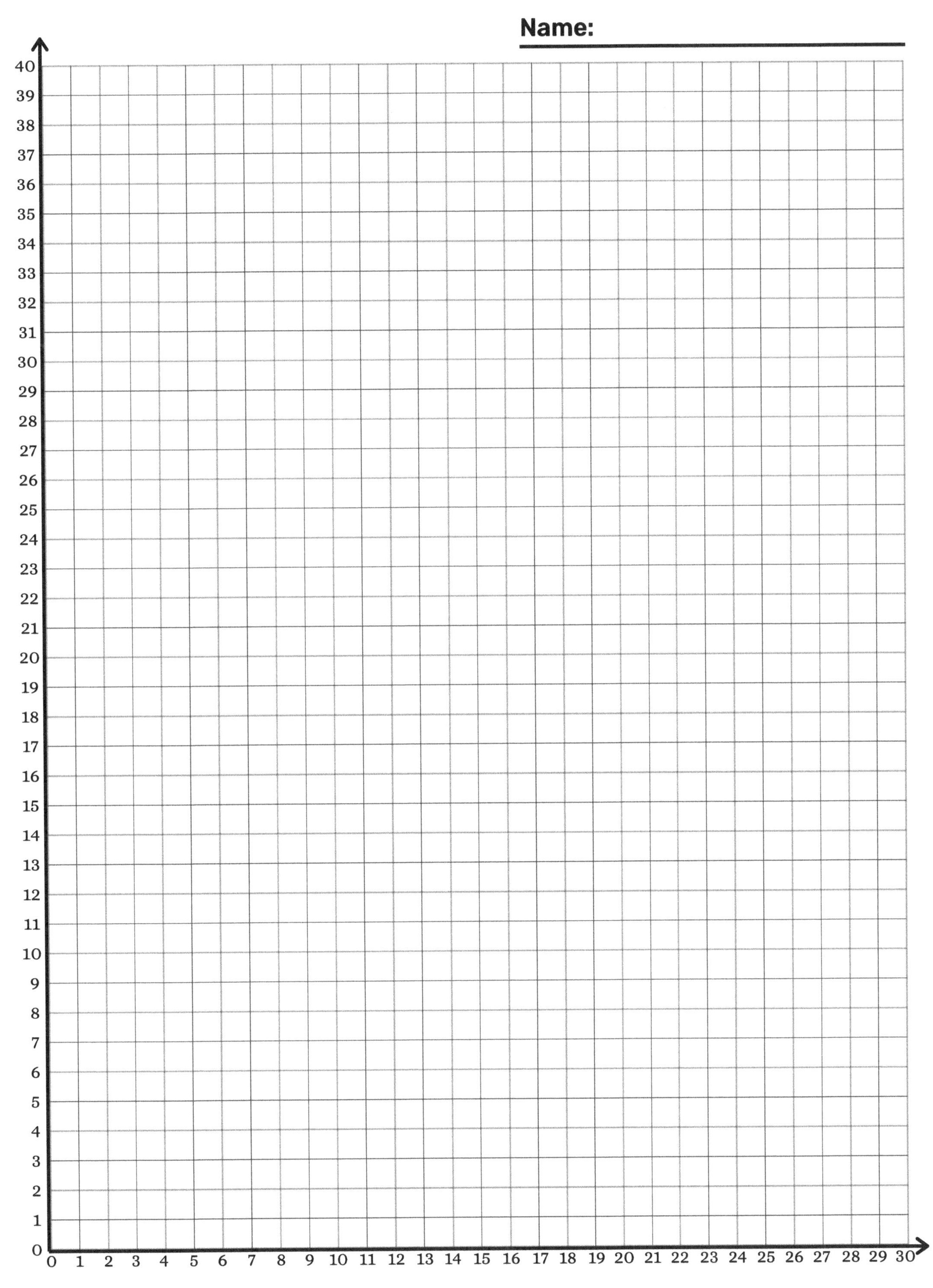

40
39
38
37
36
35
34
33
32
31
30
29
28
27
26
25
24
23
22
21
20
19
18
17
16
15
14
13
12
11
10
9
8
7
6
5
4
3
2
1
0
0 1 2 3 4 5 6 7 8 9 10 11 12 13 14 15 16 17 18 19 20 21 22 23 24 25 26 27 28 29 30

THANKSGIVING MYSTERY PICTURE #1 (FOUR QUADRANT)

Plot the ordered pairs, connecting with straight lines as you go. Be sure to stop when you reach **"STOP"** and begin a new series of connected lines at each **"START"**. *Have fun!*

START
(10, -1)
(14, -5)
(14, -11)
(-12, -11)
(-12, -2)
(-13, -2)
(-13, -1)
(-6, 6)
(-1, 6)
(-2, 5)
(-4, 5)
(-11, -2)
(-11, -10)
(14, -10)
STOP

START
(-11, -5)
(14, -5)
STOP

START
(6, 3)
(3, 6)
(1, 6)
(2, 5)
(4, 5)
STOP

START
(8, 1)
(9, 0)
STOP

START
(0, 7)
(-2, 5)
(-2, 4)
(-3, 3)
(-3, 2)
(-4, 1)
(-4, 0)
(-3, -1)
(3, -1)
(4, 0)
(4, 1)
(3, 2)
(3, 3)
(2, 4)
(2, 5)
(0, 7)
STOP

START
(7, 15)
(7, 4)
(5, 2)
(5, -2)
(6, -2)
(6, 1)
(7, 1)
(7, -2)
(8, -2)
(8, 1)
(9, 1)
(9, -2)
(10, -2)
(10, 2)
(8, 4)
(8, 15)
(7, 15)
STOP

Name: ______________________

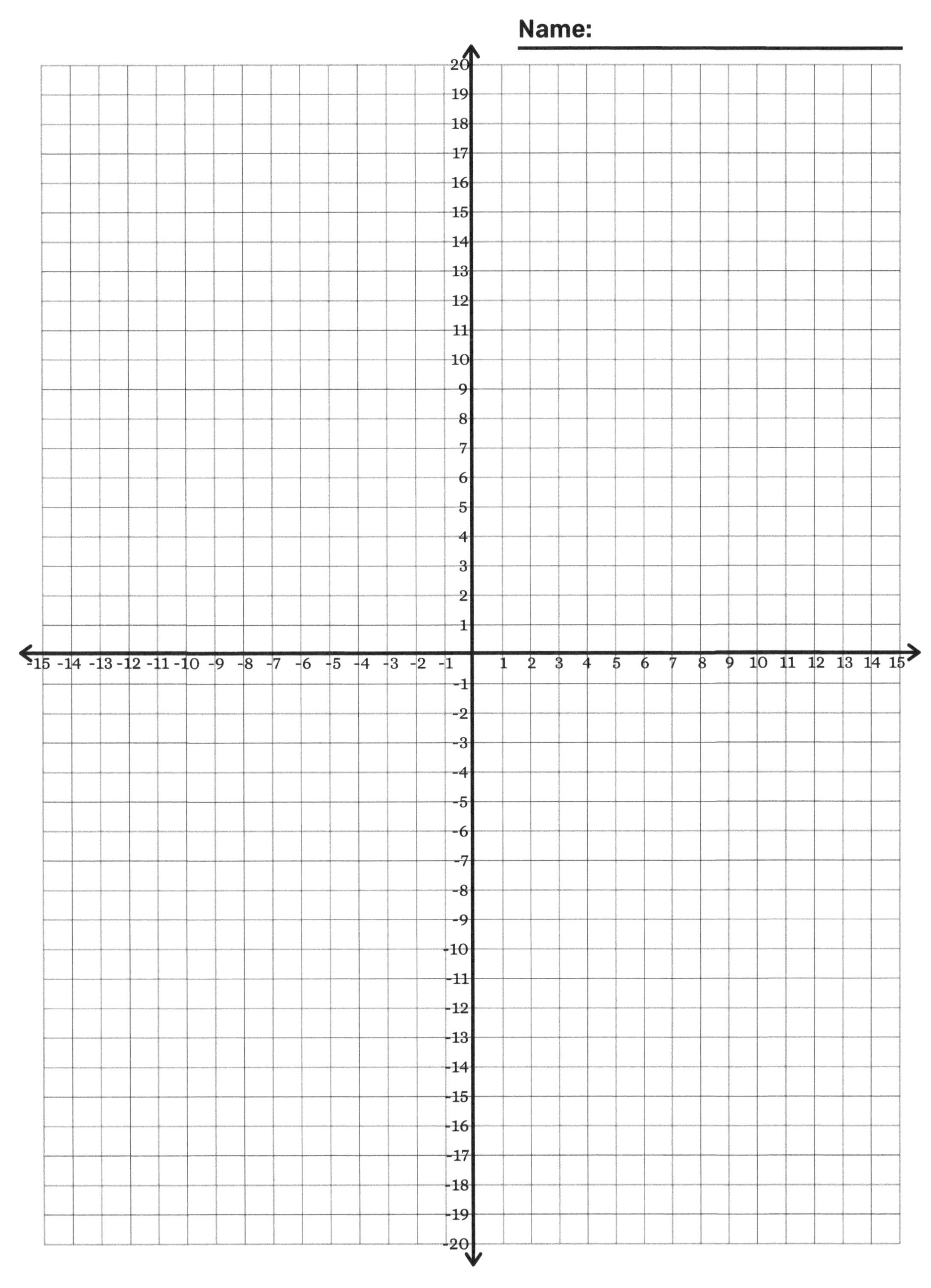

20
19
18
17
16
15
14
13
12
11
10
9
8
7
6
5
4
3
2
1
-15 -14 -13 -12 -11 -10 -9 -8 -7 -6 -5 -4 -3 -2 -1
1 2 3 4 5 6 7 8 9 10 11 12 13 14 15
-1
-2
-3
-4
-5
-6
-7
-8
-9
-10
-11
-12
-13
-14
-15
-16
-17
-18
-19
-20

THANKSGIVING MYSTERY PICTURE #2 (FIRST QUADRANT)

Plot the ordered pairs, connecting with straight lines as you go. Be sure to stop when you reach **"STOP"** and begin a new series of connected lines at each **"START"**. *Have fun!*

START
(13, 24)
(10, 24)
(7, 21)
(7, 13)
(11, 9)
(12, 9)
(13, 8)
(13, 5)
(12, 4)
(15, 4)
(14, 5)
(14, 8)
(15, 9)
(16, 9)
(17, 8)
(17, 5)
(16, 4)
(19, 4)
(18, 5)
(18, 8)
(19, 9)
(20, 9)
(24, 13)
(24, 21)
(21, 24)
(18, 24)
STOP

START
(12, 30)
(11, 29)
(11, 26)
(14, 23)
(17, 23)
(20, 26)
(20, 29)
(19, 30)
STOP

START
(11, 29)
(10, 30)
(11, 31)
(12, 31)
(12, 36)
(19, 36)
(19, 31)
(20, 31)
(21, 30)
(20, 29)
STOP

START
(10, 30)
(21, 30)
STOP

START
(12, 31)
(19, 31)
STOP

START
(12, 33)
(19, 33)
STOP

START
(14, 33)
(14, 31)
STOP

START
(15, 33)
(15, 31)
STOP

START
(16, 33)
(16, 31)
STOP

START
(17, 33)
(17, 31)
STOP

START
(12, 20)
(12, 16)
(8, 12)
STOP

START
(19, 20)
(19, 16)
(23, 12)
STOP

START
(13, 8)
(14, 8)
STOP

START
(17, 8)
(18, 8)
STOP

START
(7, 19)
(3, 23)
(3, 26)
(6, 26)
STOP

START
(9, 23)
(4, 28)
(4, 31)
(7, 31)
STOP

START
(11, 27)
(7, 31)
(7, 34)
(10, 34)
STOP

START
(12, 32)
(10, 34)
(10, 37)
(13, 37)
(14, 36)
STOP

START
(17, 36)
(18, 37)
(21, 37)
(21, 34)
STOP

START
(19, 32)
(21, 34)
(24, 34)
(24, 31)
STOP

START
(20, 27)
(24, 31)
(27, 31)
(27, 28)
(25, 26)
STOP

START
(22, 23)
(25, 26)
(28, 26)
(28, 23)
(24, 19)
STOP

START
(13, 28)
(13, 29)
(14, 29)
(14, 28)
(13, 28)
STOP

START
(17, 28)
(17, 29)
(18, 29)
(18, 28)
(17, 28)
STOP

START
(16, 28)
(16, 25)
(15, 24)
(14, 25)
(14, 27)
(15, 28)
(16, 28)
(18, 26)
(16, 26)
STOP

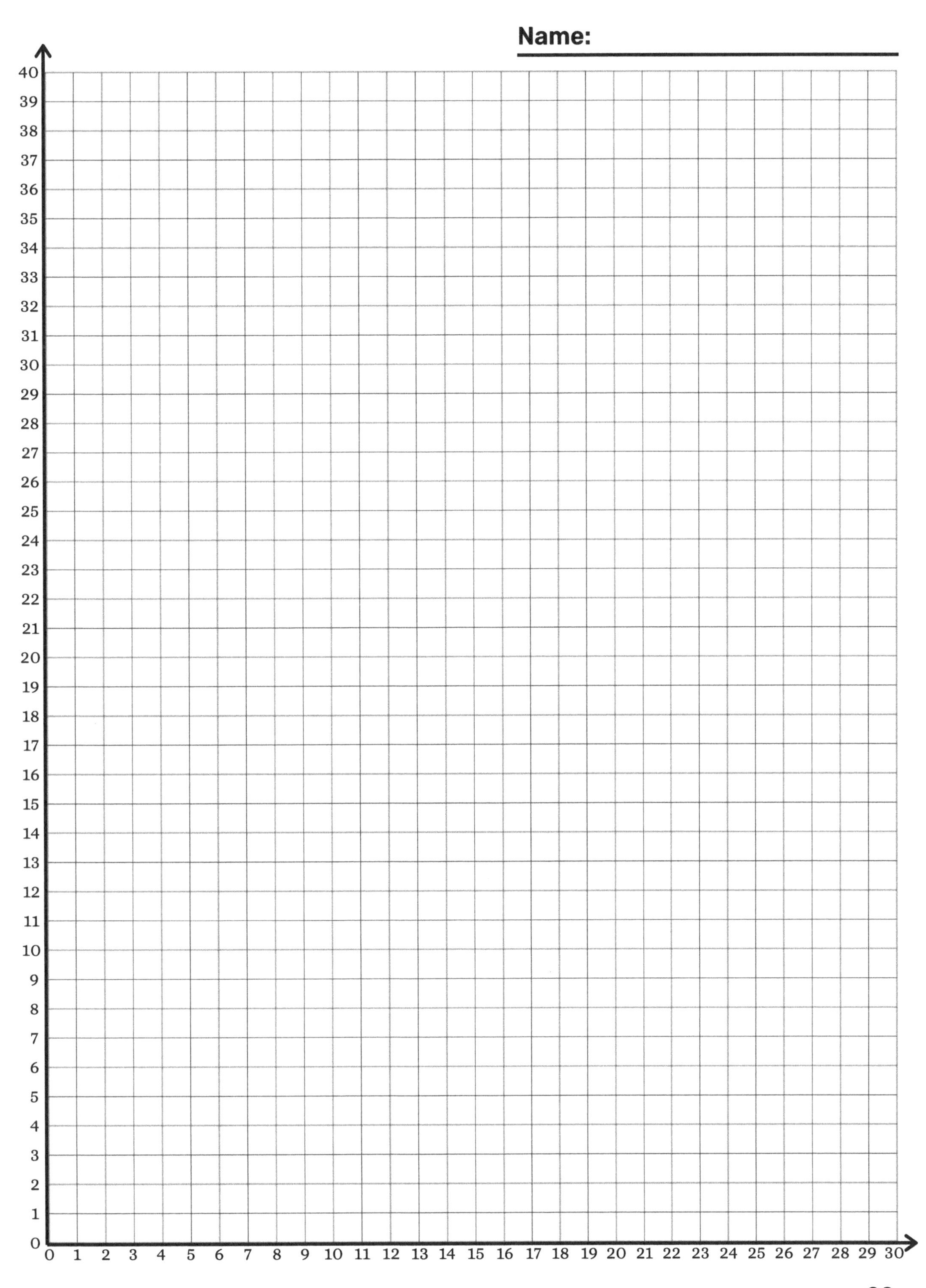
Name:
40
39
38
37
36
35
34
33
32
31
30
29
28
27
26
25
24
23
22
21
20
19
18
17
16
15
14
13
12
11
10
9
8
7
6
5
4
3
2
1
0
0 1 2 3 4 5 6 7 8 9 10 11 12 13 14 15 16 17 18 19 20 21 22 23 24 25 26 27 28 29 30

THANKSGIVING MYSTERY PICTURE #2 (FOUR QUADRANT)

Plot the ordered pairs, connecting with straight lines as you go. Be sure to stop when you reach **"STOP"** and begin a new series of connected lines at each **"START"**. *Have fun!*

START
(-2, 4)
(-5, 4)
(-8, 1)
(-8, -7)
(-4, -11)
(-3, -11)
(-2, -12)
(-2, -15)
(-3, -16)
(0, -16)
(-1, -15)
(-1, -12)
(0, -11)
(1, -11)
(2, -12)
(2, -15)
(1, -16)
(4, -16)
(3, -15)
(3, -12)
(4, -11)
(5, -11)
(9, -7)
(9, 1)
(6, 4)
(3, 4)
STOP

START
(-3, 10)
(-4, 9)
(-4, 6)
(-1, 3)
(2, 3)
(5, 6)
(5, 9)
(4, 10)
STOP

START
(-4, 9)
(-5, 10)
(-4, 11)
(-3, 11)
(-3, 16)
(4, 16)
(4, 11)
(5, 11)
(6, 10)
(5, 9)
STOP

START
(-5, 10)
(6, 10)
STOP

START
(-3, 11)
(4, 11)
STOP

START
(-3, 13)
(4, 13)
STOP

START
(-1, 13)
(-1, 11)
STOP

START
(0, 13)
(0, 11)
STOP

START
(1, 13)
(1, 11)
STOP

START
(2, 13)
(2, 11)
STOP

START
(-3, 0)
(-3, -4)
(-7, -8)
STOP

START
(4, 0)
(4, -4)
(8, -8)
STOP

START
(-2, -12)
(-1, -12)
STOP

START
(2, -12)
(3, -12)
STOP

START
(-8, -1)
(-12, 3)
(-12, 6)
(-9, 6)
STOP

START
(-6, 3)
(-11, 8)
(-11, 11)
(-8, 11)
STOP

START
(-4, 7)
(-8, 11)
(-8, 14)
(-5, 14)
STOP

START
(-3, 12)
(-5, 14)
(-5, 17)
(-2, 17)
(-1, 16)
STOP

START
(2, 16)
(3, 17)
(6, 17)
(6, 14)
STOP

START
(4, 12)
(6, 14)
(9, 14)
(9, 11)
STOP

START
(5, 7)
(9, 11)
(12, 11)
(12, 8)
(10, 6)
STOP

START
(7, 3)
(10, 6)
(13, 6)
(13, 3)
(9, -1)
STOP

START
(-2, 8)
(-2, 9)
(-1, 9)
(-1, 8)
(-2, 8)
STOP

START
(2, 8)
(2, 9)
(3, 9)
(3, 8)
(2, 8)
STOP

START
(1, 8)
(1, 5)
(0, 4)
(-1, 5)
(-1, 7)
(0, 8)
(1, 8)
(3, 6)
(1, 6)
STOP

Name: ______________________

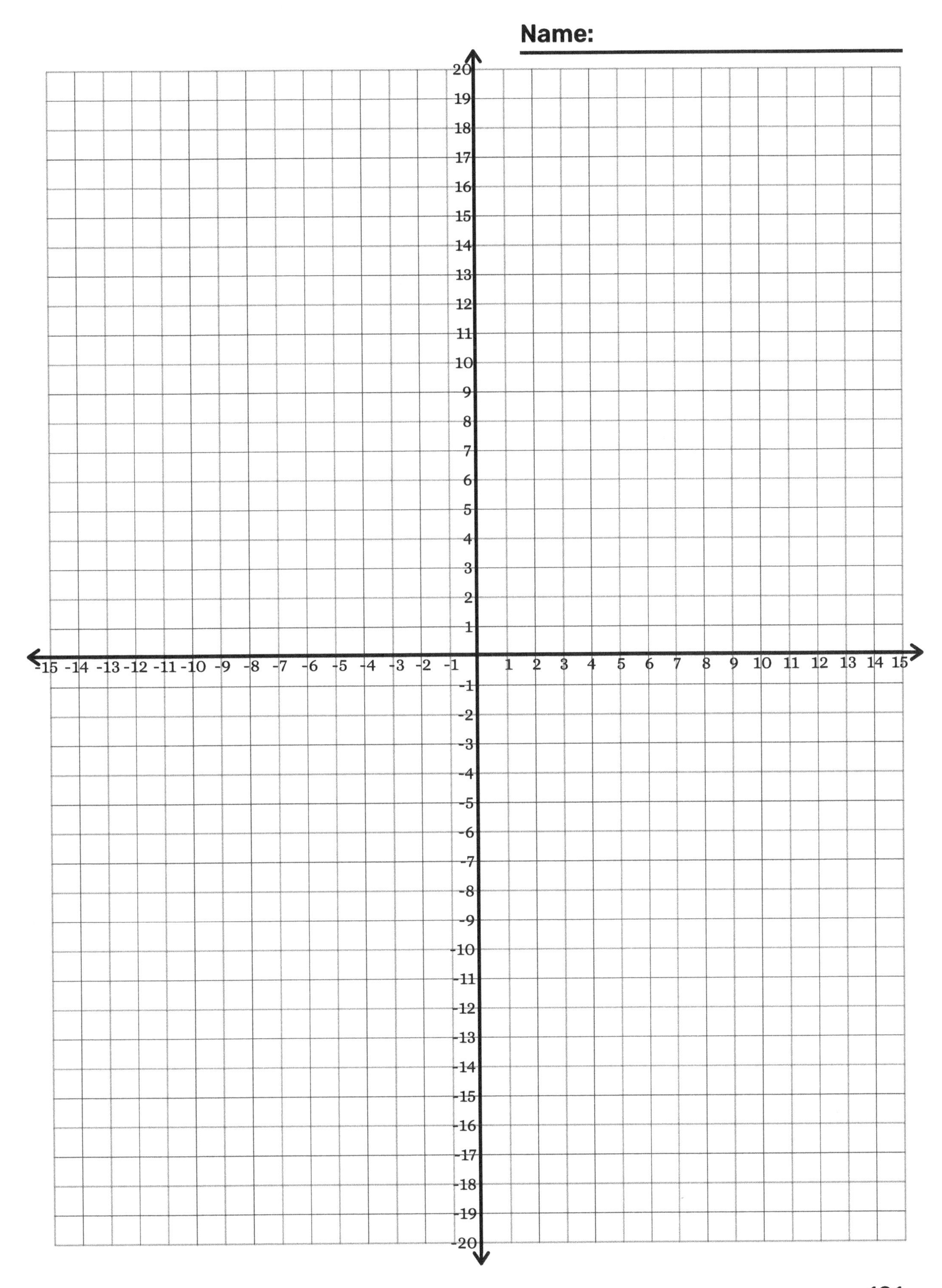

20
19
18
17
16
15
14
13
12
11
10
9
8
7
6
5
4
3
2
1
-15 -14 -13 -12 -11 -10 -9 -8 -7 -6 -5 -4 -3 -2 -1
1 2 3 4 5 6 7 8 9 10 11 12 13 14 15
-1
-2
-3
-4
-5
-6
-7
-8
-9
-10
-11
-12
-13
-14
-15
-16
-17
-18
-19
-20

CHRISTMAS MYSTERY PICTURE #1 (FIRST QUADRANT)

Plot the ordered pairs, connecting with straight lines as you go. Be sure to stop when you reach **"STOP"** and begin a new series of connected lines at each **"START"**. *Have fun!*

START	**START**	**START**	**START**	**START**	**START**
(12, 24)	(12, 30)	(5, 24)	(6, 12)	(24, 12)	(14, 14)
(9, 27)	(11, 31)	(4, 23)	(7, 12)	(23, 12)	(14, 16)
(9, 33)	(11, 32)	(5, 22)	(7, 11)	(23, 11)	(16, 16)
(12, 36)	(12, 33)	(4, 21)	(8, 11)	(22, 11)	(16, 14)
(18, 36)	(13, 33)	(5, 20)	(8, 10)	(22, 10)	(14, 14)
(21, 33)	(14, 32)	(4, 19)	(9, 10)	(21, 10)	**STOP**
(21, 27)	(14, 31)	(5, 18)	(9, 9)	(21, 9)	
(18, 24)	(13, 30)	(4, 17)	(10, 9)	(20, 9)	**START**
(27, 24)	(12, 30)	(5, 17)	(10, 8)	(20, 8)	(12, 25)
(29, 22)	**STOP**	(6, 18)	(11, 8)	(19, 8)	(13, 25)
(29, 19)		(5, 19)	(11, 7)	(19, 7)	(14, 24)
(27, 17)	**START**	(6, 20)	(12, 7)	(18, 7)	(16, 24)
(19, 17)	(17, 30)	(5, 21)	(12, 6)	(18, 6)	(17, 25)
(25, 11)	(16, 31)	(6, 22)	(13, 7)	(17, 7)	(18, 25)
(27, 11)	(16, 32)	(5, 23)	(13, 8)	(17, 8)	(18, 22)
(29, 9)	(17, 33)	(6, 24)	(12, 8)	(18, 8)	(17, 22)
(29, 6)	(18, 33)	**STOP**	(12, 9)	(18, 9)	(16, 23)
(27, 4)	(19, 32)		(11, 9)	(19, 9)	(14, 23)
(20, 4)	(19, 31)	**START**	(11, 10)	(19, 10)	(13, 22)
(15, 9)	(18, 30)	(24, 24)	(10, 10)	(20, 10)	(12, 22)
(10, 4)	(17, 30)	(23, 23)	(10, 11)	(20, 11)	(12, 25)
(3, 4)	**STOP**	(24, 22)	(9, 11)	(21, 11)	**STOP**
(1, 6)		(23, 21)	(9, 12)	(21, 12)	
(1, 9)	**START**	(24, 20)	(8, 12)	(22, 12)	**START**
(3, 11)	(13, 28)	(23, 19)	(8, 13)	(22, 13)	(14, 24)
(5, 11)	(14, 27)	(24, 18)	(7, 13)	(23, 13)	(14, 23)
(11, 17)	(16, 27)	(23, 17)	**STOP**	**STOP**	**STOP**
(3, 17)	(17, 28)	(24, 17)			
(1, 19)	**STOP**	(25, 18)	**START**	**START**	**START**
(1, 22)		(24, 19)	(14, 20)	(14, 17)	(16, 24)
(3, 24)		(25, 20)	(14, 22)	(14, 19)	(16, 23)
(12, 24)		(24, 21)	(16, 22)	(16, 19)	**STOP**
STOP		(25, 22)	(16, 20)	(16, 17)	
		(24, 23)	(14, 20)	(14, 17)	
		(25, 24)	**STOP**	**STOP**	
		STOP			

Name: ____________________

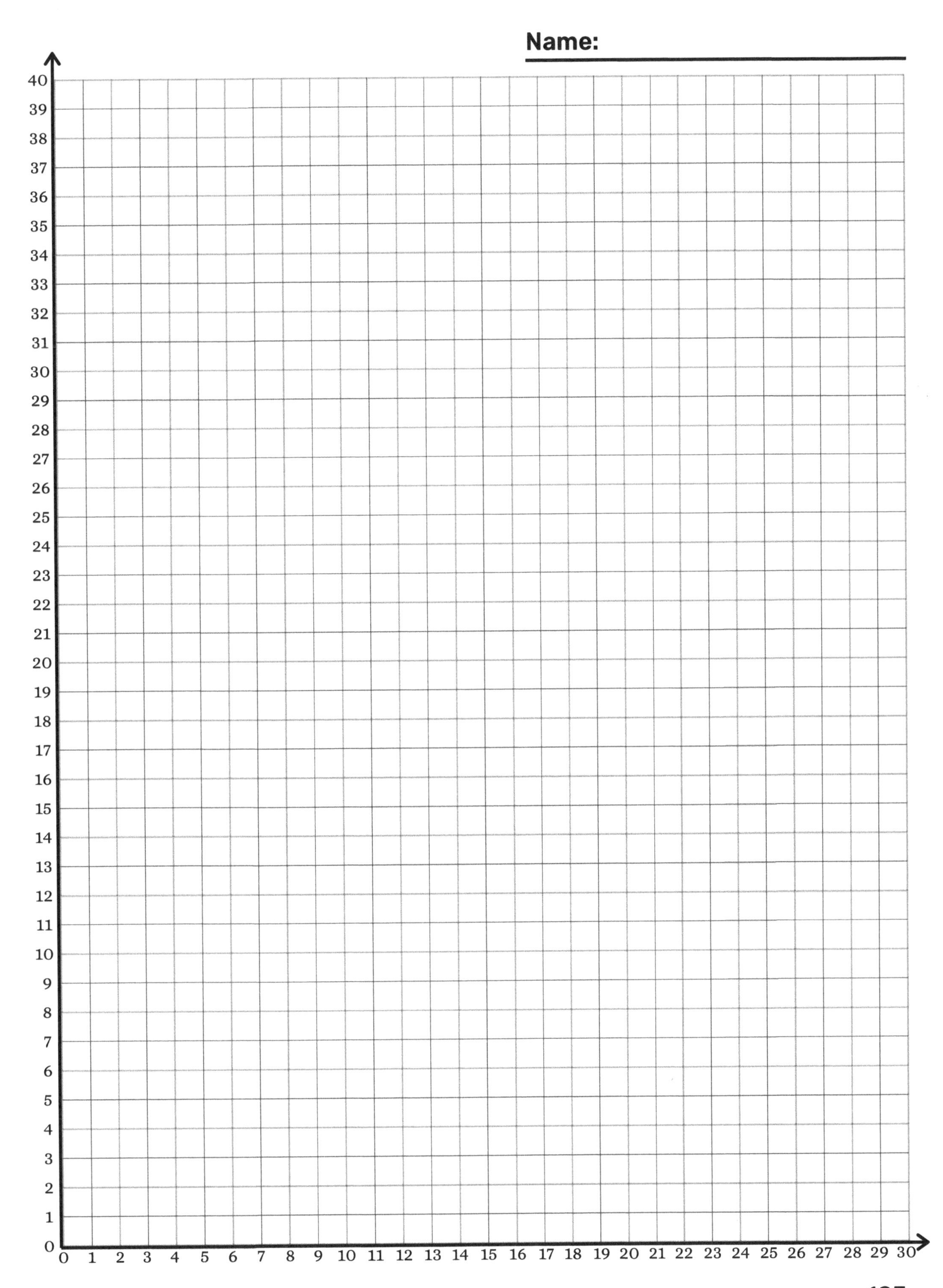

40
39
38
37
36
35
34
33
32
31
30
29
28
27
26
25
24
23
22
21
20
19
18
17
16
15
14
13
12
11
10
9
8
7
6
5
4
3
2
1
0
0 1 2 3 4 5 6 7 8 9 10 11 12 13 14 15 16 17 18 19 20 21 22 23 24 25 26 27 28 29 30

CHRISTMAS MYSTERY PICTURE #1 (FOUR QUADRANT)

Plot the ordered pairs, connecting with straight lines as you go. Be sure to stop when you reach **"STOP"** and begin a new series of connected lines at each **"START"**. *Have fun!*

START	**START**	**START**	**START**	**START**	**START**
(-3, 4)	(-3, 10)	(-10, 4)	(-9, -8)	(9, -8)	(-1, -6)
(-6, 7)	(-4, 11)	(-11, 3)	(-8, -8)	(8, -8)	(-1, -4)
(-6, 13)	(-4, 12)	(-10, 2)	(-8, -9)	(8, -9)	(1, -4)
(-3, 16)	(-3, 13)	(-11, 1)	(-7, -9)	(7, -9)	(1, -6)
(3, 16)	(-2, 13)	(-10, 0)	(-7, -10)	(7, -10)	(-1, -6)
(6, 13)	(-1, 12)	(-11, -1)	(-6, -10)	(6, -10)	**STOP**
(6, 7)	(-1, 11)	(-10, -2)	(-6, -11)	(6, -11)	
(3, 4)	(-2, 10)	(-11, -3)	(-5, -11)	(5, -11)	**START**
(12, 4)	(-3, 10)	(-10, -3)	(-5, -12)	(5, -12)	(-3, 5)
(14, 2)	**STOP**	(-9, -2)	(-4, -12)	(4, -12)	(-2, 5)
(14, -1)		(-10, -1)	(-4, -13)	(4, -13)	(-1, 4)
(12, -3)	**START**	(-9, 0)	(-3, -13)	(3, -13)	(1, 4)
(4, -3)	(2, 10)	(-10, 1)	(-3, -14)	(3, -14)	(2, 5)
(10, -9)	(1, 11)	(-9, 2)	(-2, -13)	(2, -13)	(3, 5)
(12, -9)	(1, 12)	(-10, 3)	(-2, -12)	(2, -12)	(3, 2)
(14, -11)	(2, 13)	(-9, 4)	(-3, -12)	(3, -12)	(2, 2)
(14, -14)	(3, 13)	**STOP**	(-3, -11)	(3, -11)	(1, 3)
(12, -16)	(4, 12)		(-4, -11)	(4, -11)	(-1, 3)
(5, -16)	(4, 11)	**START**	(-4, -10)	(4, -10)	(-2, 2)
(0, -11)	(3, 10)	(9, 4)	(-5, -10)	(5, -10)	(-3, 2)
(-5, -16)	(2, 10)	(8, 3)	(-5, -9)	(5, -9)	(-3, 5)
(-12, -16)	**STOP**	(9, 2)	(-6, -9)	(6, -9)	**STOP**
(-14, -14)		(8, 1)	(-6, -8)	(6, -8)	
(-14, -11)	**START**	(9, 0)	(-7, -8)	(7, -8)	**START**
(-12, -9)	(-2, 8)	(8, -1)	(-7, -7)	(7, -7)	(-1, 4)
(-10, -9)	(-1, 7)	(9, -2)	(-8, -7)	(8, -7)	(-1, 3)
(-4, -3)	(1, 7)	(8, -3)	**STOP**	**STOP**	**STOP**
(-12, -3)	(2, 8)	(9, -3)			
(-14, -1)	**STOP**	(10, -2)	**START**	**START**	**START**
(-14, 2)		(9, -1)	(-1, 0)	(-1, -3)	(1, 4)
(-12, 4)		(10, 0)	(-1, 2)	(-1, -1)	(1, 3)
(-3, 4)		(9, 1)	(1, 2)	(1, -1)	**STOP**
STOP		(10, 2)	(1, 0)	(1, -3)	
		(9, 3)	(-1, 0)	(-1, -3)	
		(10, 4)	**STOP**	**STOP**	
		STOP			

Name: ______________________________

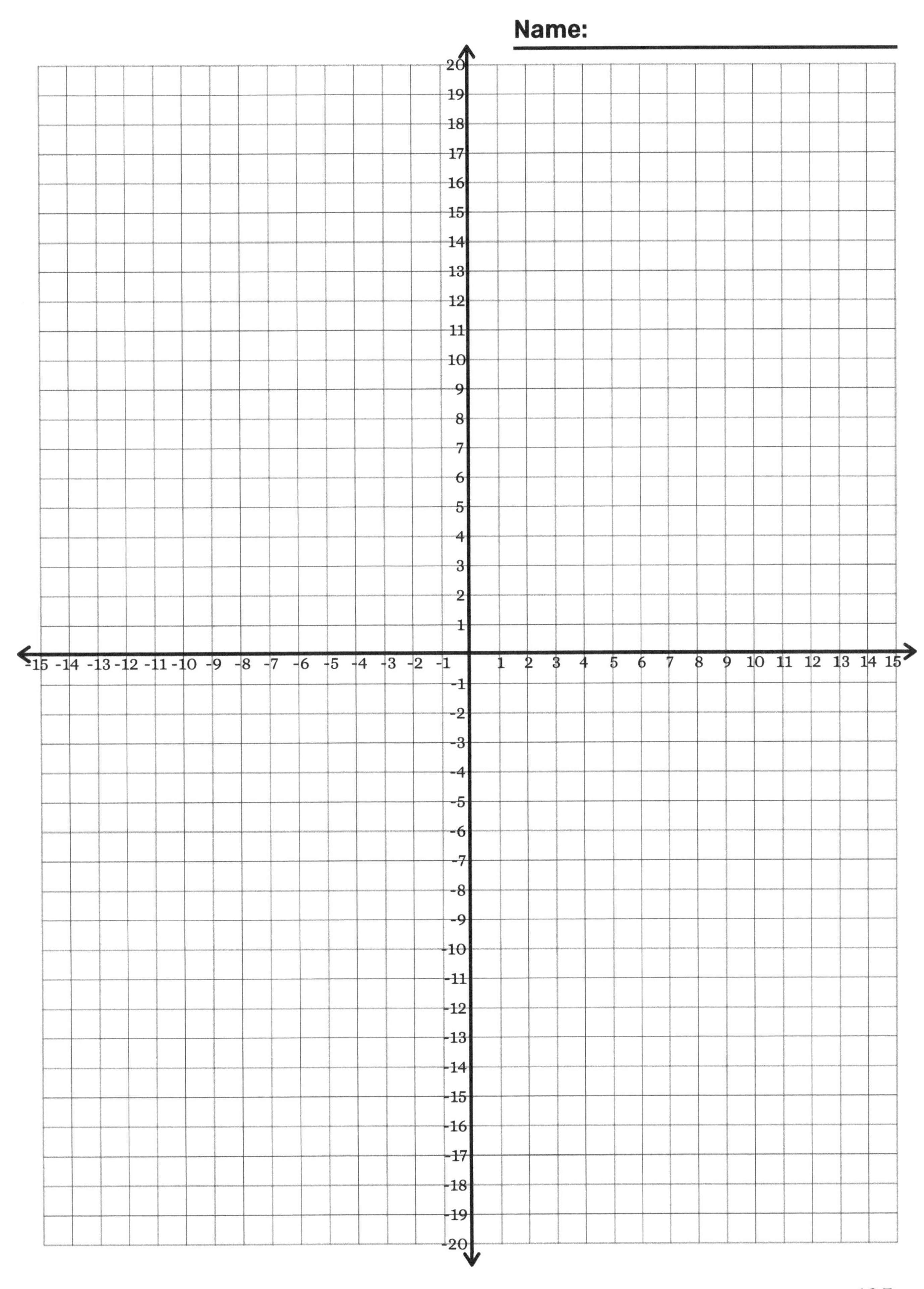

20
19
18
17
16
15
14
13
12
11
10
9
8
7
6
5
4
3
2
1
-15 -14 -13 -12 -11 -10 -9 -8 -7 -6 -5 -4 -3 -2 -1
1 2 3 4 5 6 7 8 9 10 11 12 13 14 15
-1
-2
-3
-4
-5
-6
-7
-8
-9
-10
-11
-12
-13
-14
-15
-16
-17
-18
-19
-20

CHRISTMAS MYSTERY PICTURE #2 (FIRST QUADRANT)

Plot the ordered pairs, connecting with straight lines as you go. Be sure to stop when you reach **"STOP"** and begin a new series of connected lines at each **"START"**. *Have fun!*

START
(5, 20)
(1, 16)
(2, 16)
(2, 10)
(7, 5)
(9, 5)
(12, 2)
(20, 2)
(19, 3)
(21, 5)
(23, 5)
(28, 10)
(28, 16)
(29, 16)
(25, 20)
STOP

START
(10, 17)
(13, 14)
(17, 14)
(20, 17)
STOP

START
(12, 15)
(18, 15)
STOP

START
(5, 22)
(5, 20)
(6, 19)
(5, 19)
(7, 17)
(14, 17)
(15, 18)
(16, 17)
(23, 17)
(25, 19)
(24, 19)
(25, 20)
(25, 22)
(23, 22)
(22, 21)
(17, 21)
(17, 20)
(16, 19)
(14, 19)
(13, 20)
(13, 21)
(8, 21)
(7, 22)
(5, 22)
STOP

START
(24, 22)
(24, 25)
(22, 27)
(8, 27)
(6, 25)
(5, 26)
(6, 25)
(6, 22)
STOP

START
(24, 25)
(25, 26)
(25, 30)
(24, 31)
(23, 31)
(23, 32)
(16, 39)
(6, 39)
(2, 35)
(2, 28)
(3, 28)
(6, 31)
(23, 31)
STOP

START
(5, 27)
(4, 28)
(1, 28)
(0, 27)
(0, 24)
(1, 23)
(4, 23)
(5, 24)
(5, 30)
STOP

START
(8, 27)
(8, 21)
STOP

START
(22, 27)
(22, 21)
STOP

START
(14, 23)
(14, 25)
(13, 26)
(11, 26)
(10, 25)
(10, 23)
(11, 22)
(13, 22)
(13, 21)
(13, 22)
(14, 23)
(16, 23)
(16, 25)
(17, 26)
(19, 26)
(20, 25)
(20, 23)
(19, 22)
(17, 22)
(17, 21)
(17, 22)
(16, 23)
STOP

START
(11, 22)
(11, 24)
(13, 24)
(13, 22)
STOP

START
(17, 22)
(17, 24)
(19, 24)
(19, 22)
STOP

Name: ______________________

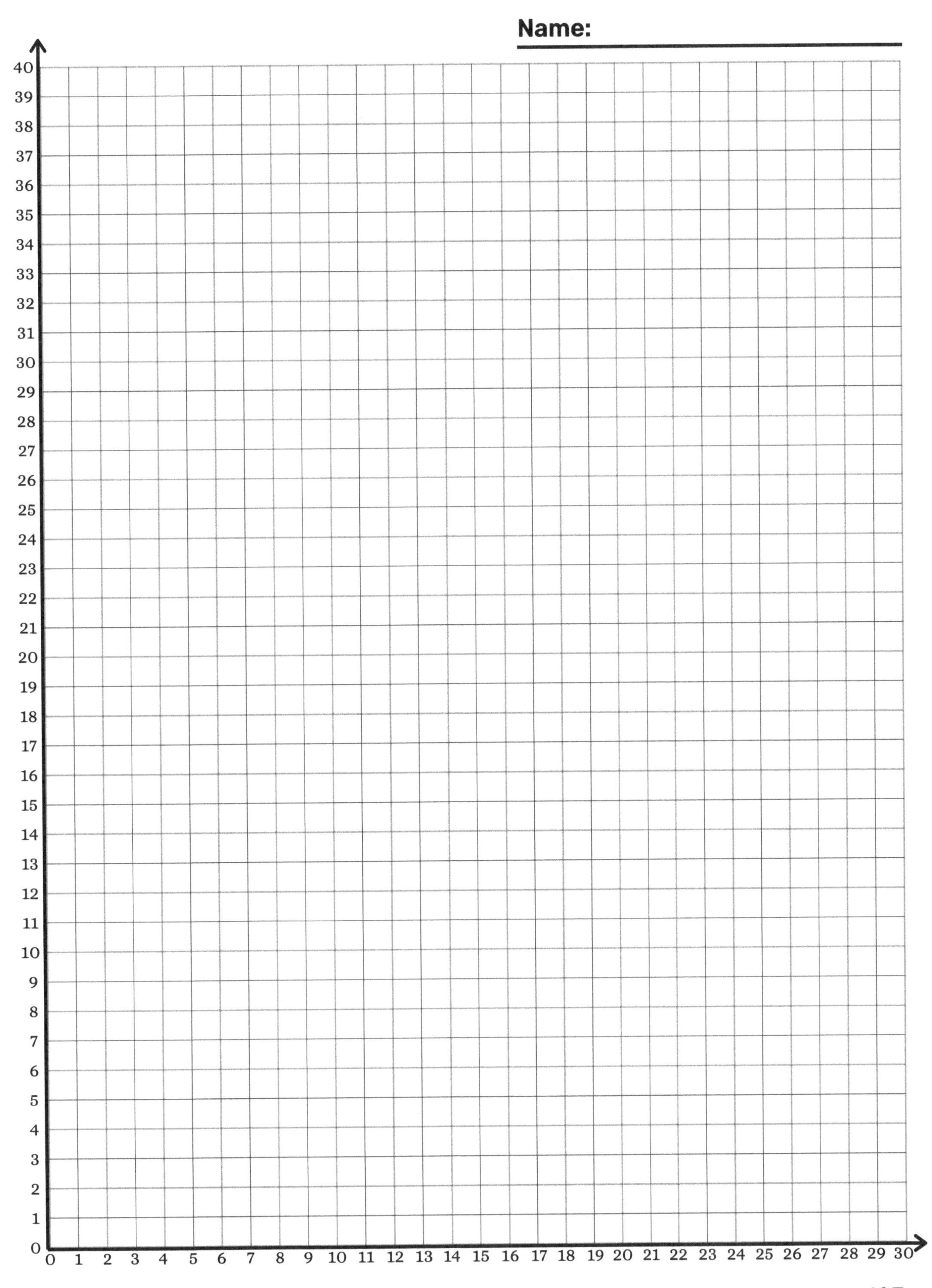

0 1 2 3 4 5 6 7 8 9 10 11 12 13 14 15 16 17 18 19 20 21 22 23 24 25 26 27 28 29 30
0 1 2 3 4 5 6 7 8 9 10 11 12 13 14 15 16 17 18 19 20 21 22 23 24 25 26 27 28 29 30 31 32 33 34 35 36 37 38 39 40

CHRISTMAS MYSTERY PICTURE #2 (FOUR QUADRANT)

Plot the ordered pairs, connecting with straight lines as you go. Be sure to stop when you reach **"STOP"** and begin a new series of connected lines at each **"START"**. *Have fun!*

START	**START**	**START**	**START**
(-10, 0)	(-10, 2)	(9, 5)	(-1, 3)
(-14, -4)	(-10, 0)	(10, 6)	(-1, 5)
(-13, -4)	(-9, -1)	(10, 10)	(-2, 6)
(-13, -10)	(-10, -1)	(9, 11)	(-4, 6)
(-8, -15)	(-8, -3)	(8, 11)	(-5, 5)
(-6, -15)	(-1, -3)	(8, 12)	(-5, 3)
(-3, -18)	(0, -2)	(1, 19)	(-4, 2)
(5, -18)	(1, -3)	(-9, 19)	(-2, 2)
(4, -17)	(8, -3)	(-13, 15)	(-2, 1)
(6, -15)	(10, -1)	(-13, 8)	(-2, 2)
(8, -15)	(9, -1)	(-12, 8)	(-1, 3)
(13, -10)	(10, 0)	(-9, 11)	(1, 3)
(13, -4)	(10, 2)	(8, 11)	(1, 5)
(14, -4)	(8, 2)	**STOP**	(2, 6)
(10, 0)	(7, 1)		(4, 6)
STOP	(2, 1)	**START**	(5, 5)
	(2, 0)	(-10, 7)	(5, 3)
START	(1, -1)	(-11, 8)	(4, 2)
(-5, -3)	(-1, -1)	(-14, 8)	(2, 2)
(-2, -6)	(-2, 0)	(-15, 7)	(2, 1)
(2, -6)	(-2, 1)	(-15, 4)	(2, 2)
(5, -3)	(-7, 1)	(-14, 3)	(1, 3)
STOP	(-8, 2)	(-11, 3)	**STOP**
	(-10, 2)	(-10, 4)	
START	**STOP**	(-10, 10)	**START**
(-3, -5)		**STOP**	(-4, 2)
(3, -5)	**START**		(-4, 4)
STOP	(9, 2)	**START**	(-2, 4)
	(9, 5)	(-7, 7)	(-2, 2)
	(7, 7)	(-7, 1)	**STOP**
	(-7, 7)	**STOP**	
	(-9, 5)		**START**
	(-10, 6)	**START**	(2, 2)
	(-9, 5)	(7, 7)	(2, 4)
	(-9, 2)	(7, 1)	(4, 4)
	STOP	**STOP**	(4, 2)
			STOP

Name: ______________________________

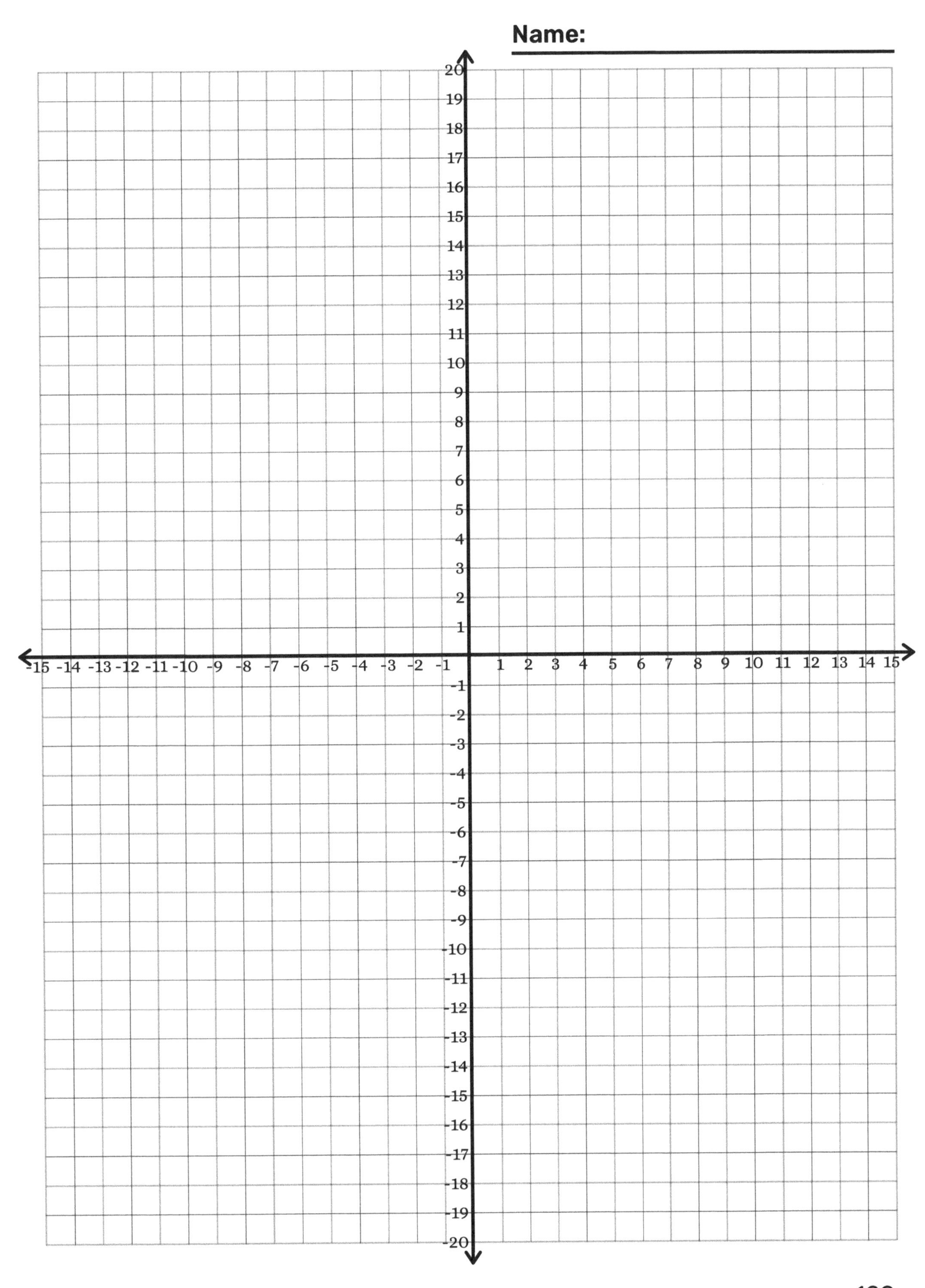

-15 -14 -13 -12 -11 -10 -9 -8 -7 -6 -5 -4 -3 -2 -1 1 2 3 4 5 6 7 8 9 10 11 12 13 14 15
20 19 18 17 16 15 14 13 12 11 10 9 8 7 6 5 4 3 2 1 -1 -2 -3 -4 -5 -6 -7 -8 -9 -10 -11 -12 -13 -14 -15 -16 -17 -18 -19 -20

Answer Key

WINTER MYSTERY PICTURE #1

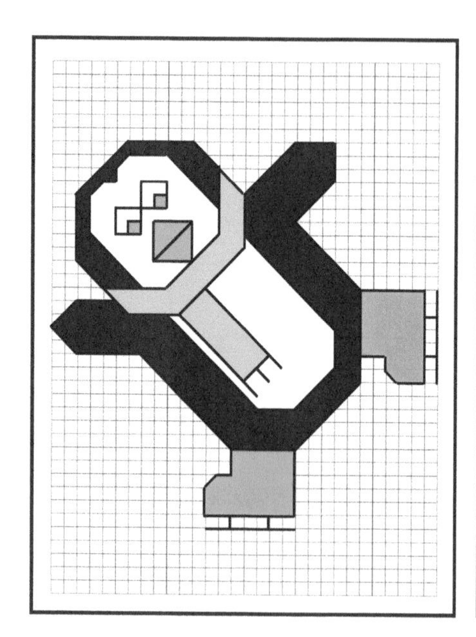

PAGE 7

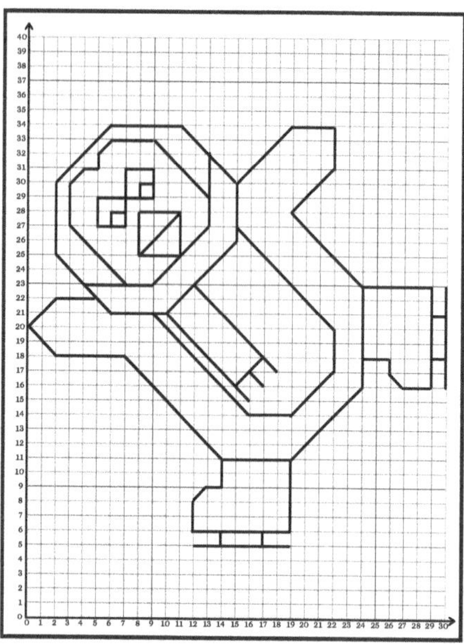

PAGE 9

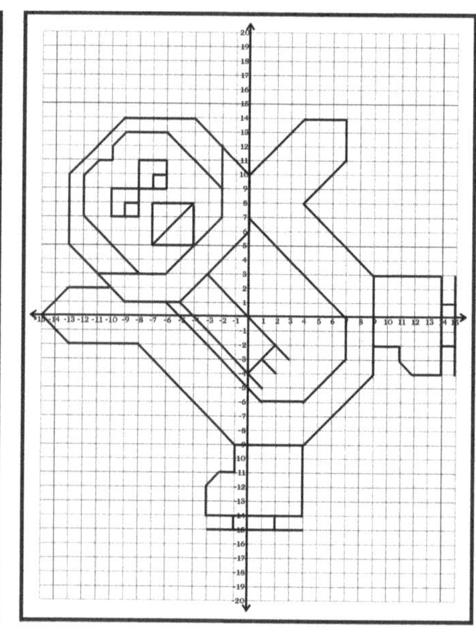

WINTER MYSTERY PICTURE #2

PAGE 11

PAGE 13

VALENTINE'S DAY MYSTERY PICTURE #1

PAGE 15

PAGE 17

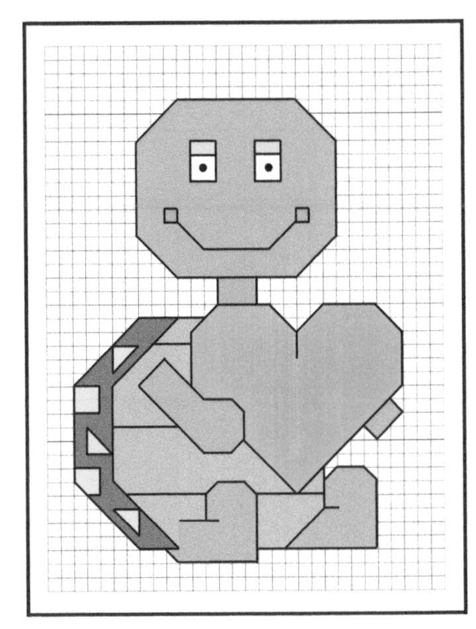

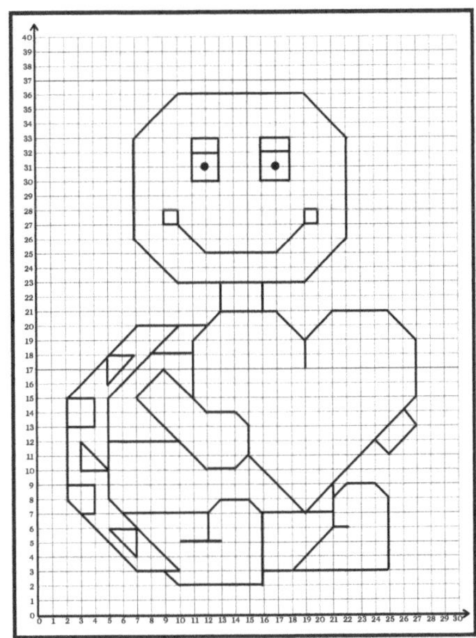

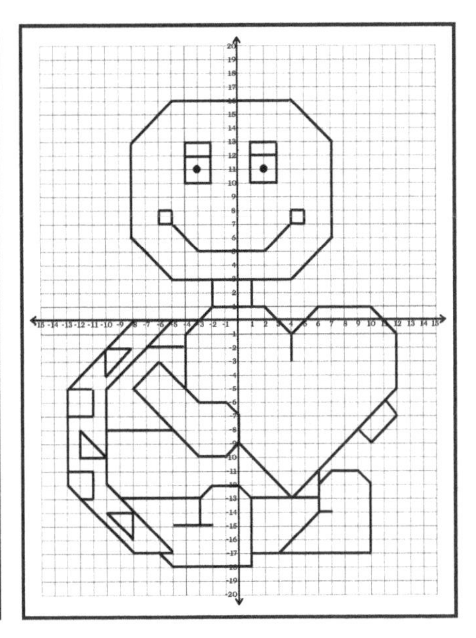

VALENTINE'S DAY MYSTERY PICTURE #2

PAGE 19

PAGE 21

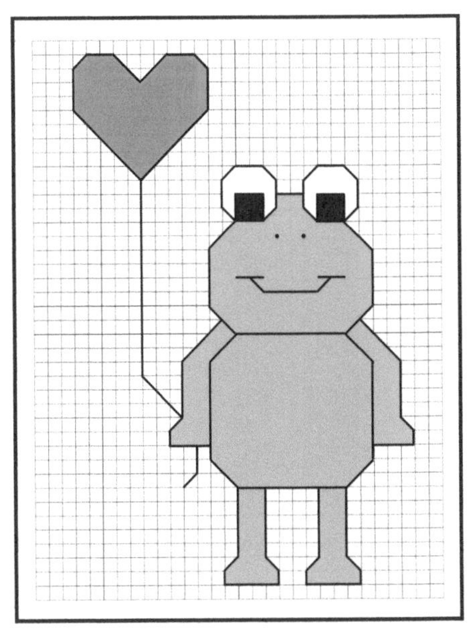

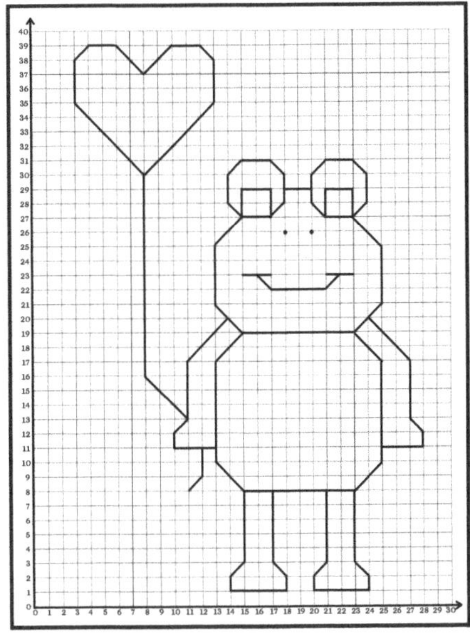

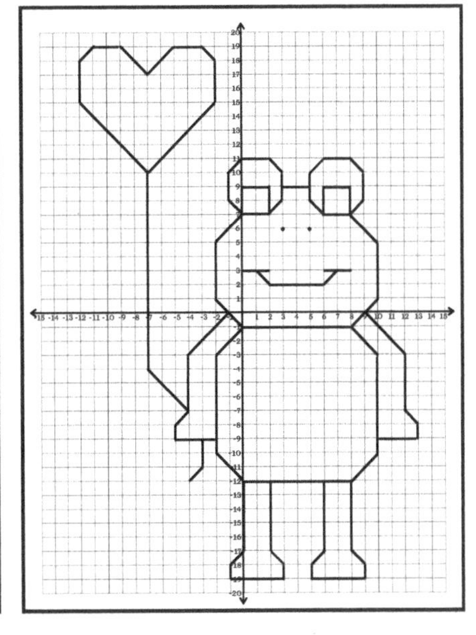

PRESIDENT'S DAY MYSTERY PICTURE #1

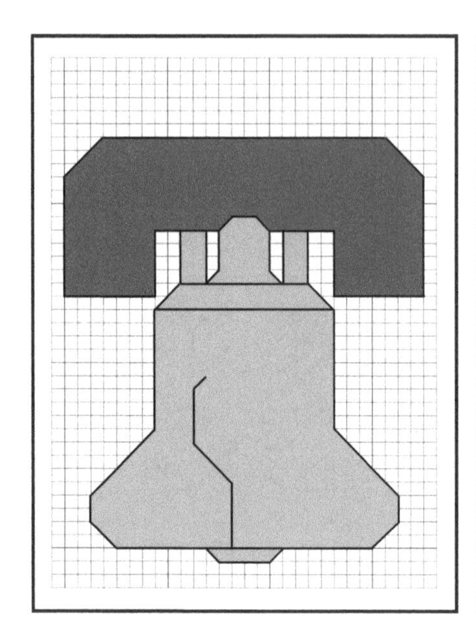

PAGE 23

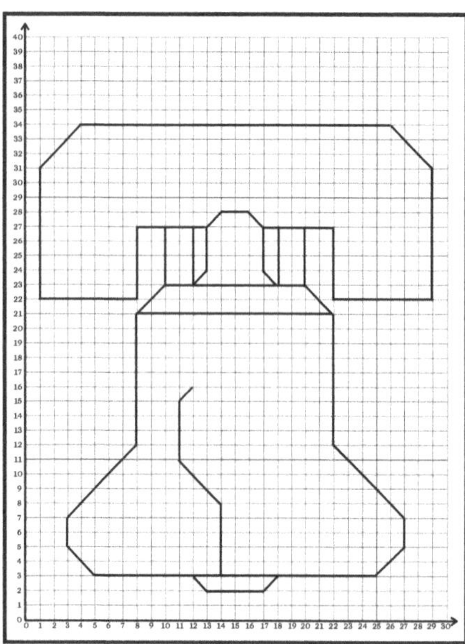

PAGE 25

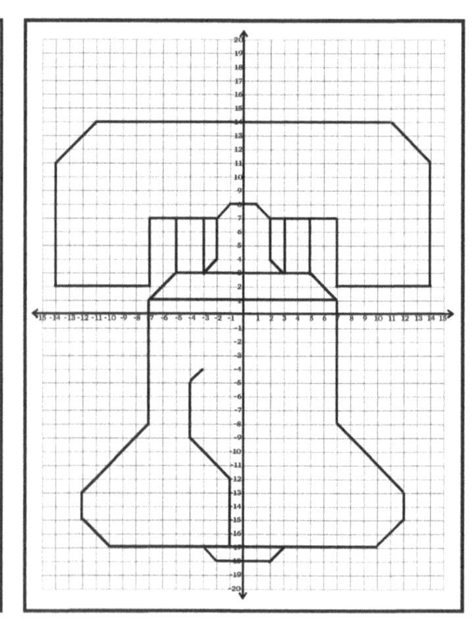

PRESIDENT'S DAY MYSTERY PICTURE #2

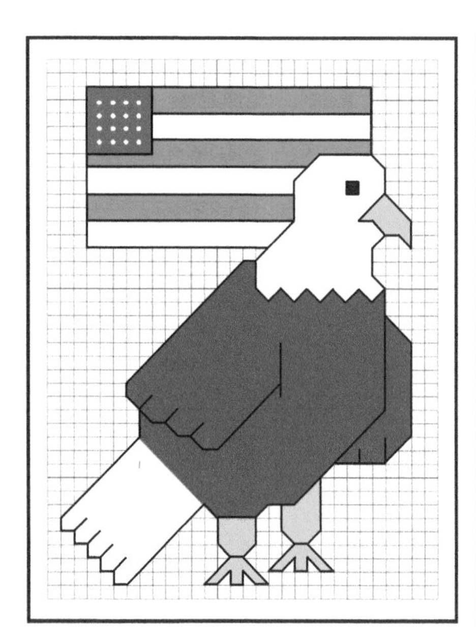

PAGE 27

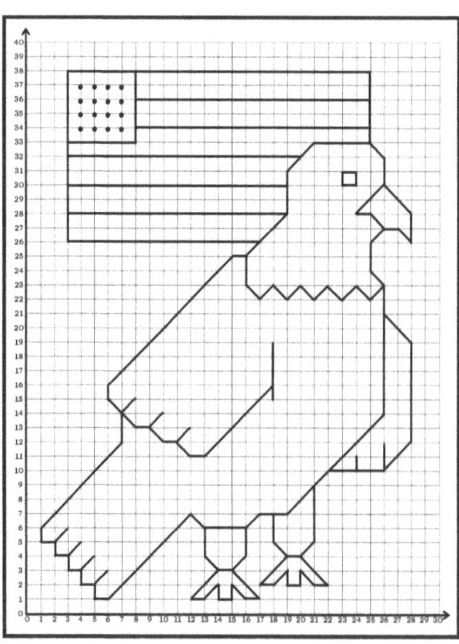

PAGE 29

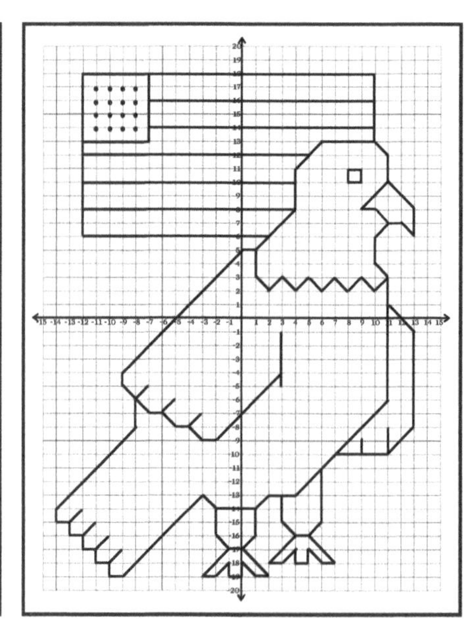

ST. PATRICK'S DAY MYSTERY PICTURE #1

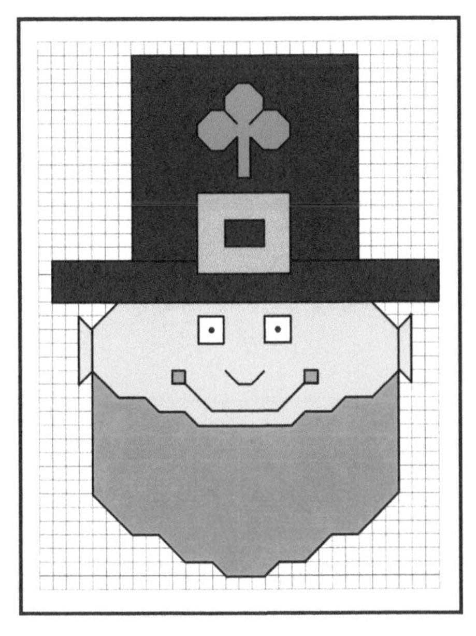

PAGE 31

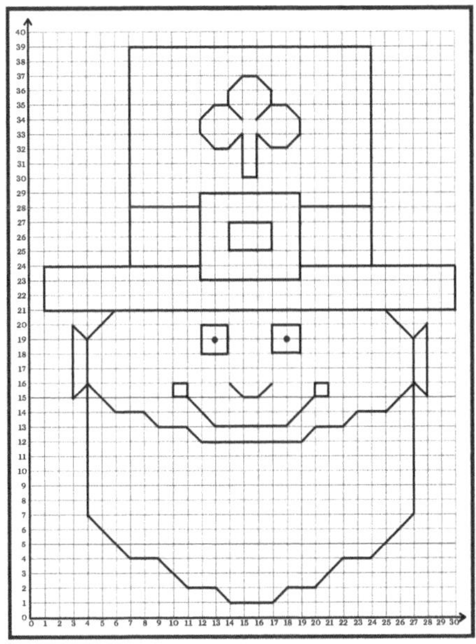

PAGE 33

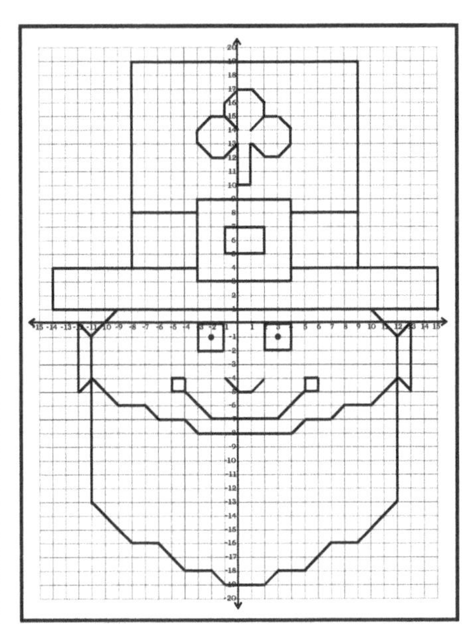

ST. PATRICK'S DAY MYSTERY PICTURE #2

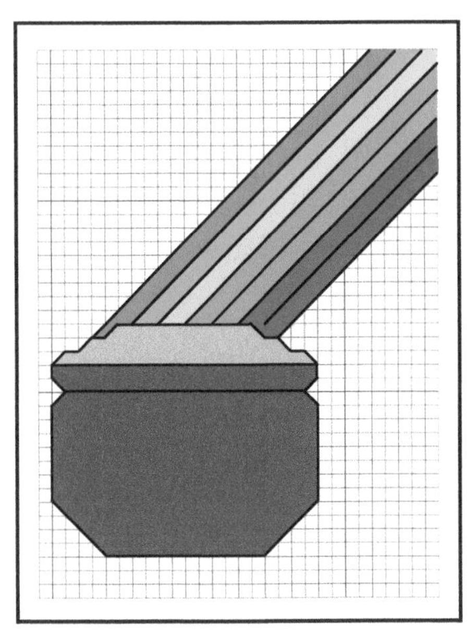

PAGE 35

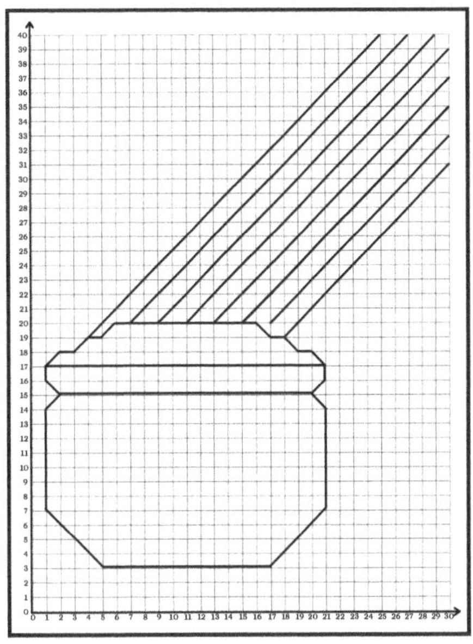

PAGE 37

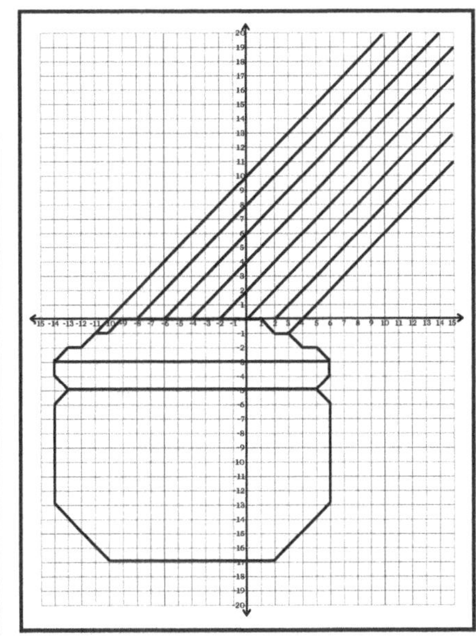

SPRING MYSTERY PICTURE #1

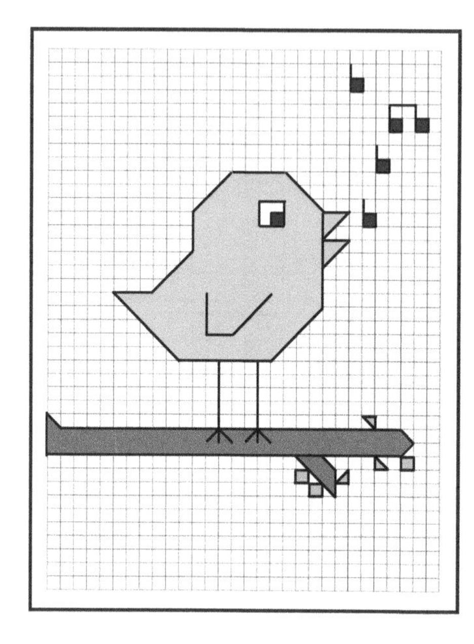

PAGE 39

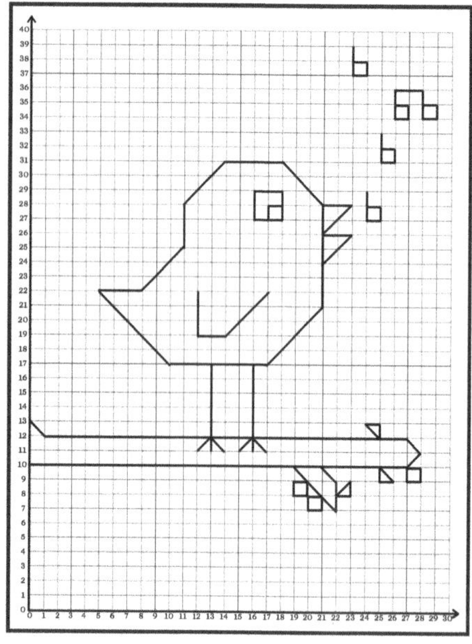

PAGE 41

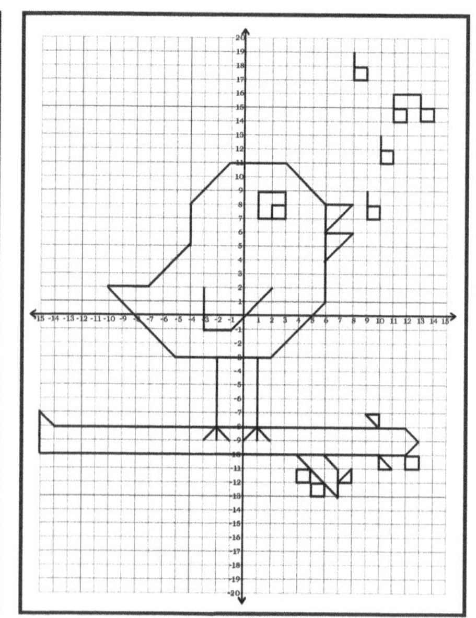

SPRING MYSTERY PICTURE #2

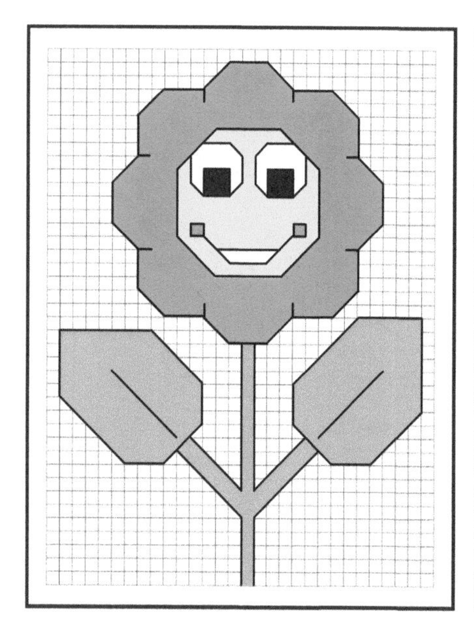

PAGE 43

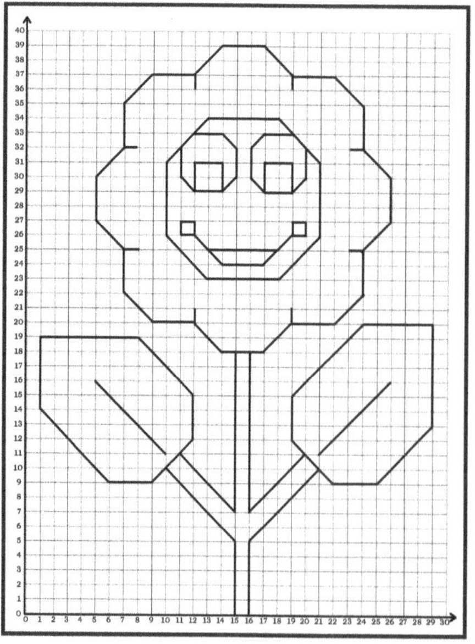

PAGE 45

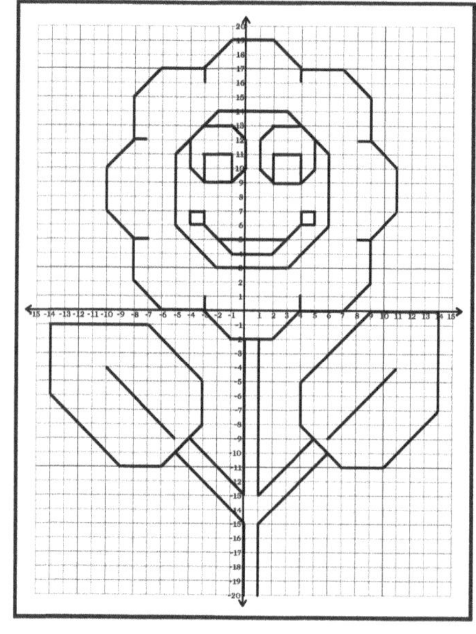

PUPPY PALS MYSTERY PICTURE #1

PAGE 47

PAGE 49

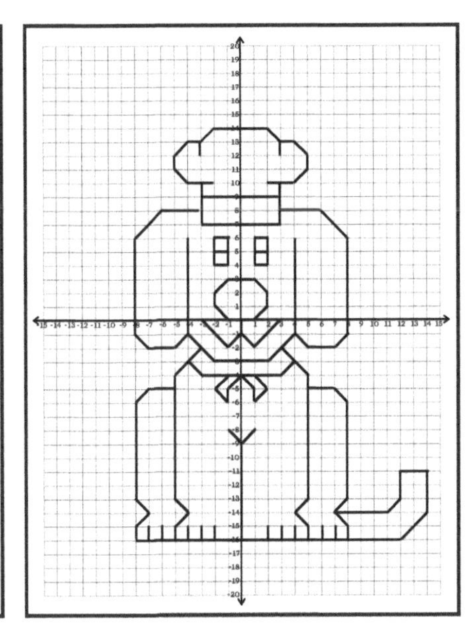

PUPPY PALS MYSTERY PICTURE #2

PAGE 51

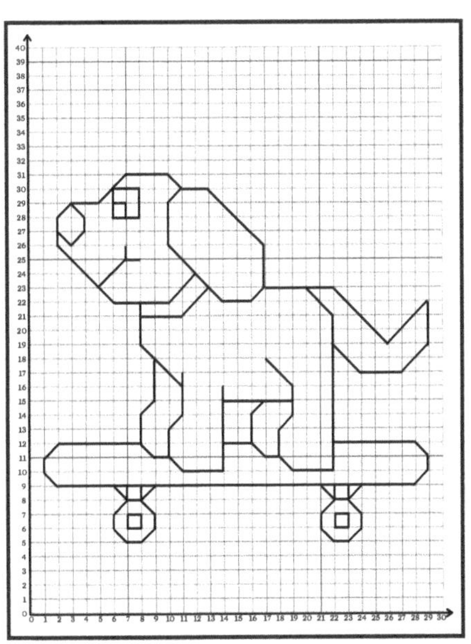

PAGE 53

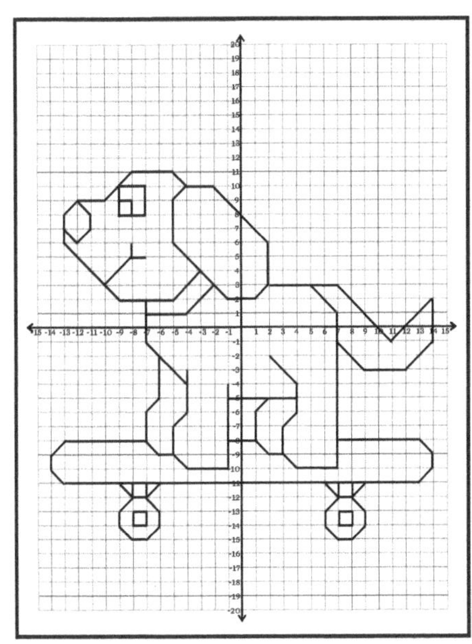

PUPPY PALS MYSTERY PICTURE #3

PAGE 55

PAGE 57

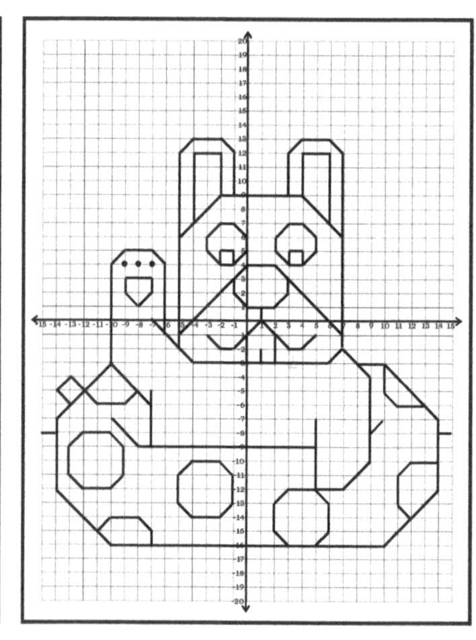

PUPPY PALS MYSTERY PICTURE #4

PAGE 59

PAGE 61

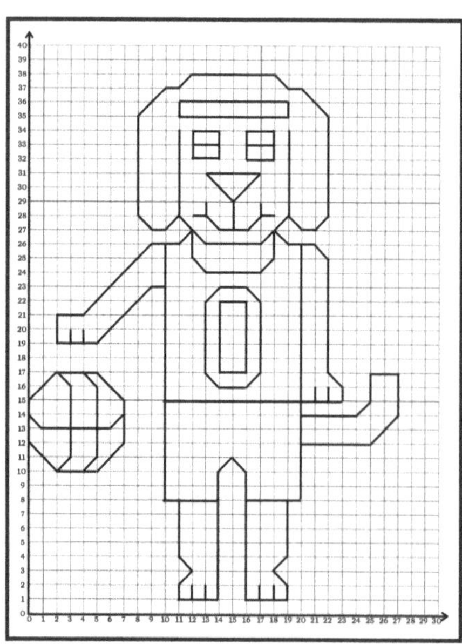

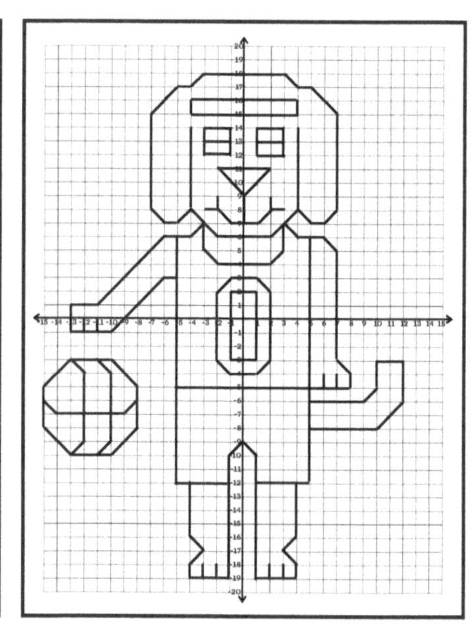

SUMMER MYSTERY PICTURE #1

PAGE 63

PAGE 65

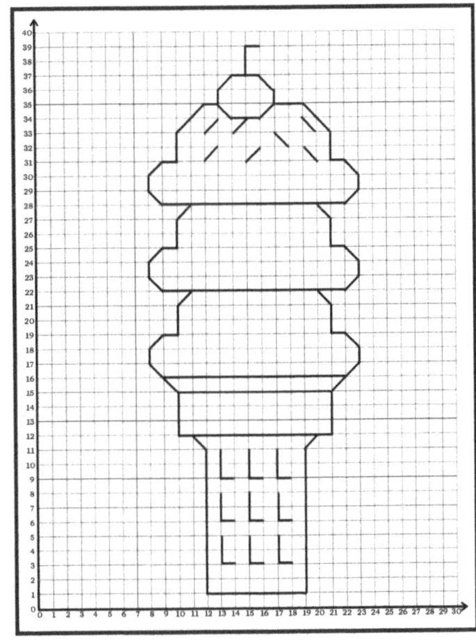

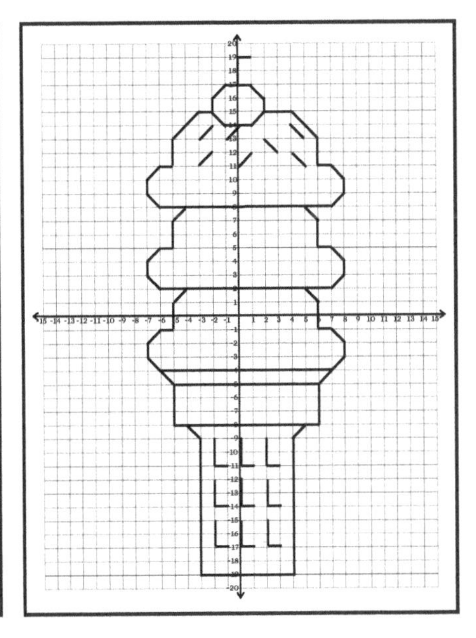

SUMMER MYSTERY PICTURE #2

PAGE 67

PAGE 69

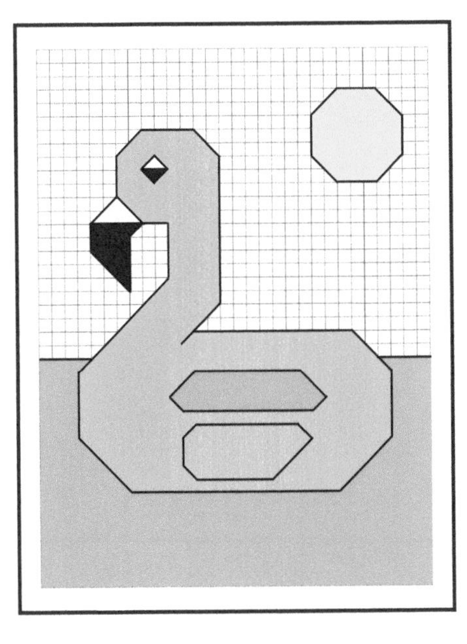

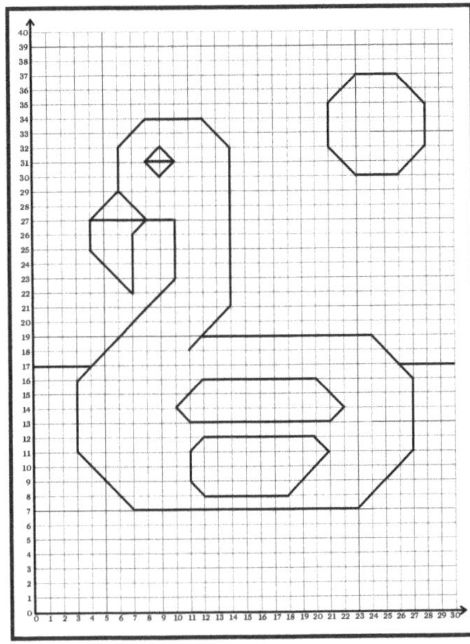

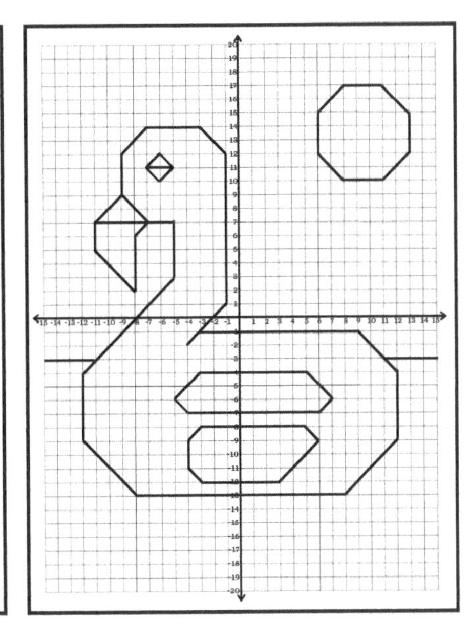

FALL MYSTERY PICTURE #1

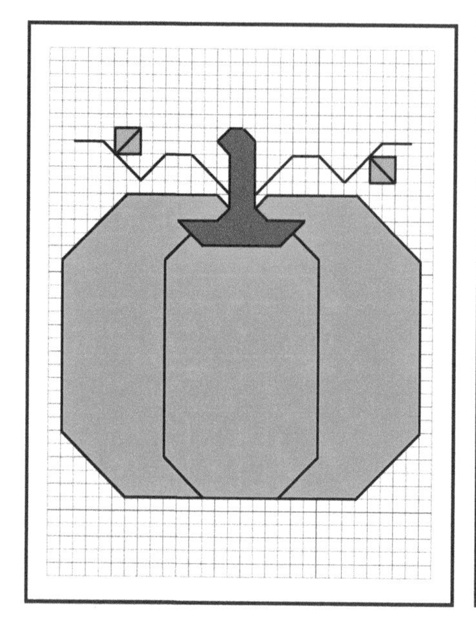

PAGE 71

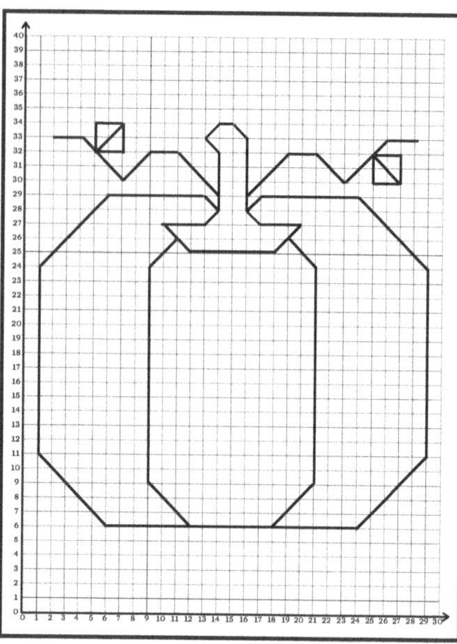

PAGE 73

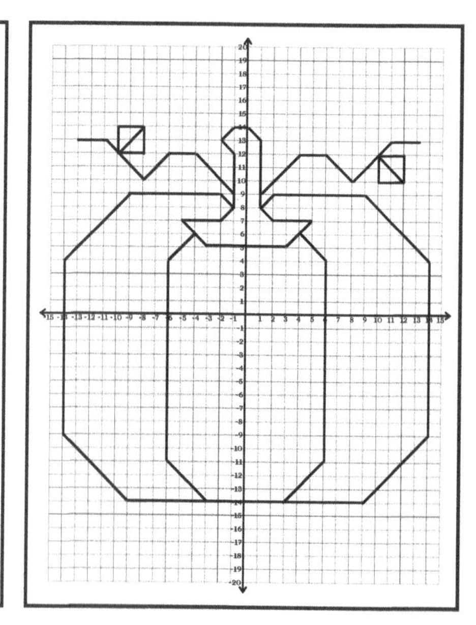

FALL MYSTERY PICTURE #2

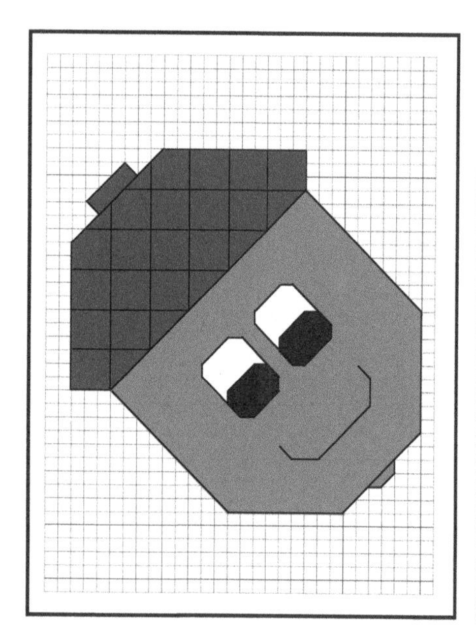

PAGE 75

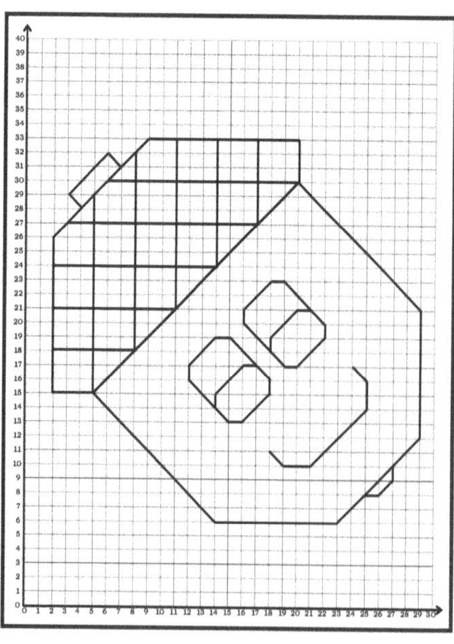

PAGE 77

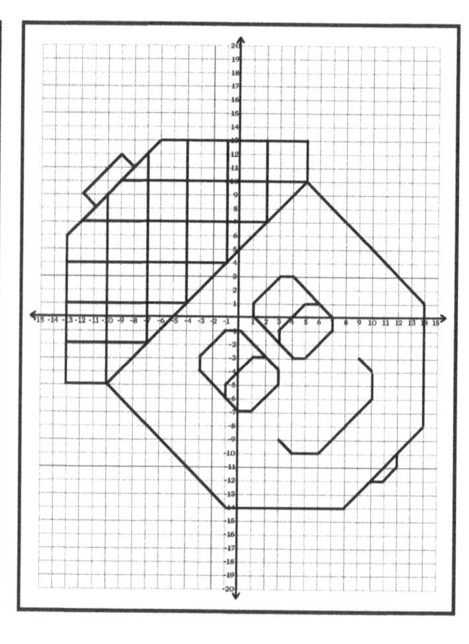

FALL MYSTERY PICTURE #3

PAGE 79

PAGE 81

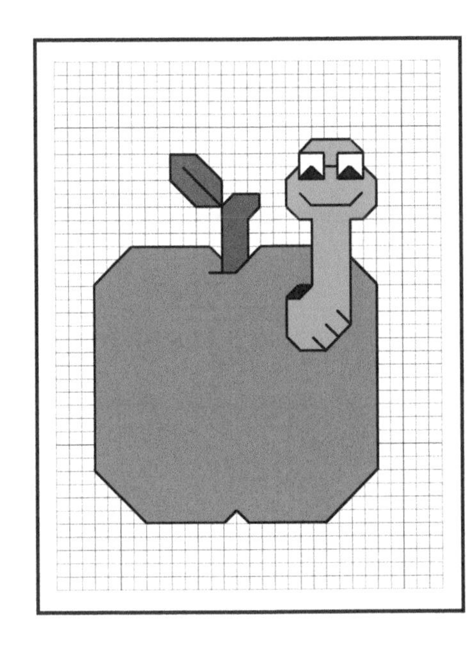

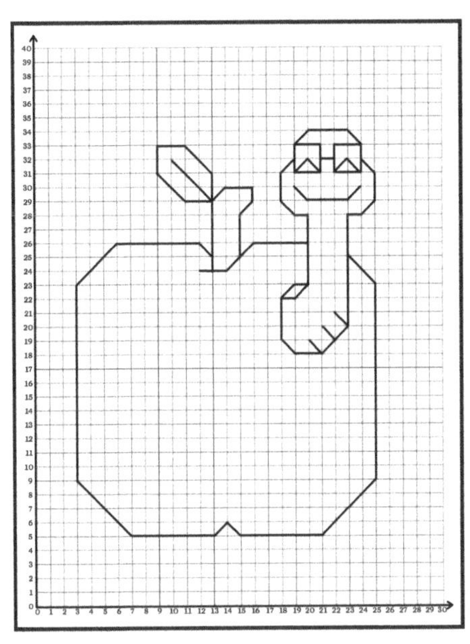

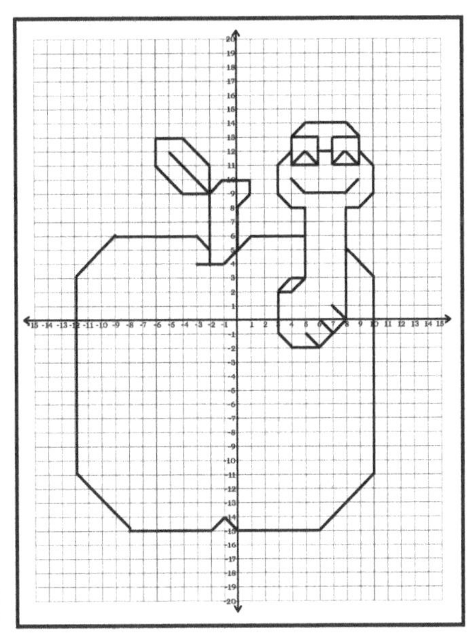

FALL MYSTERY PICTURE #4

PAGE 83

PAGE 85

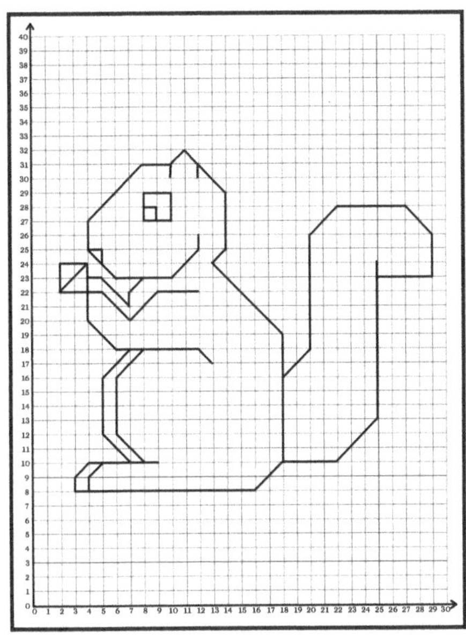

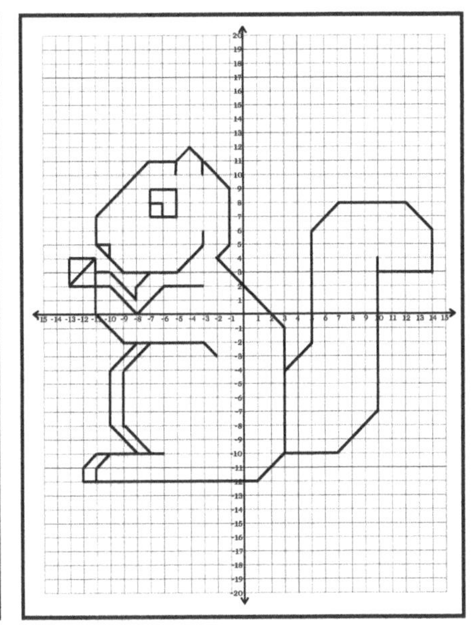

HALLOWEEN MYSTERY PICTURE #1

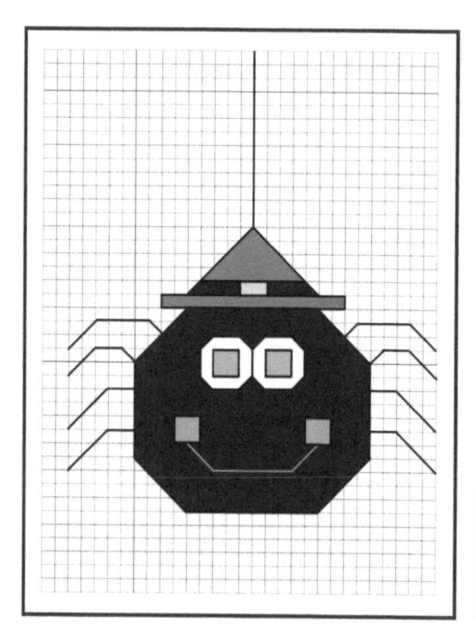

PAGE 87

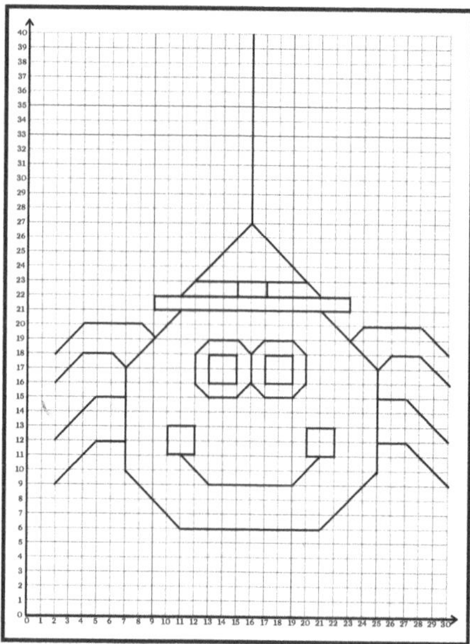

PAGE 89

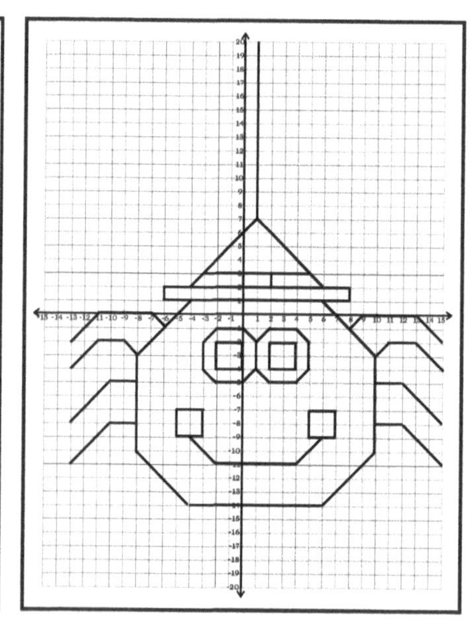

HALLOWEEN MYSTERY PICTURE #2

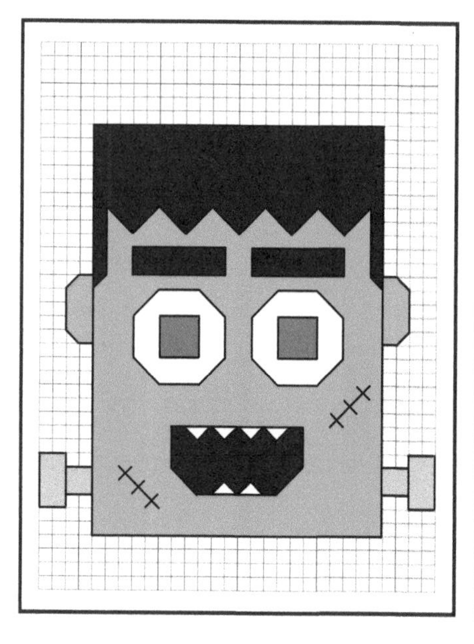

PAGE 91

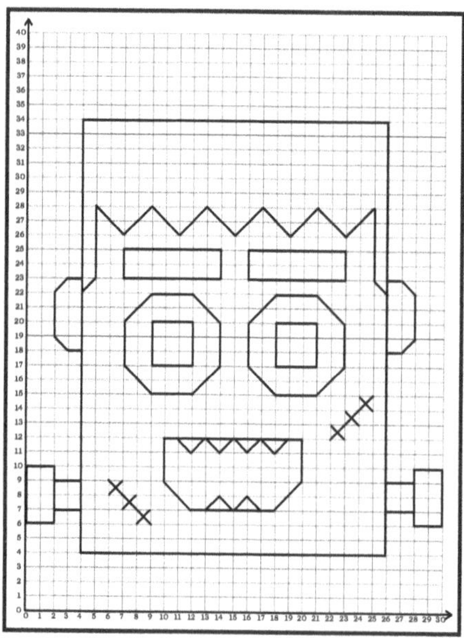

PAGE 93

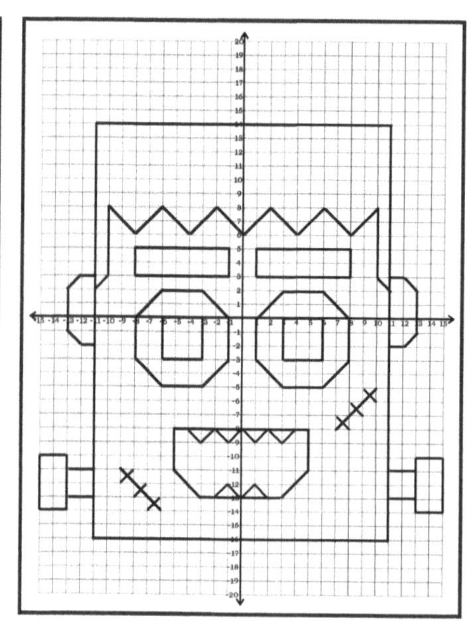

THANKSGIVING MYSTERY PICTURE #1

PAGE 95

PAGE 97

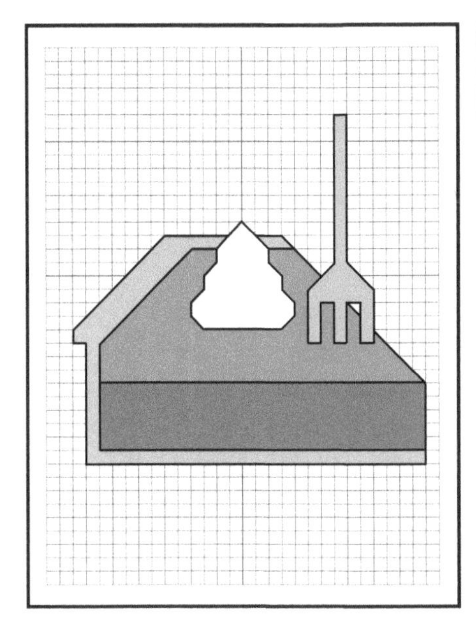

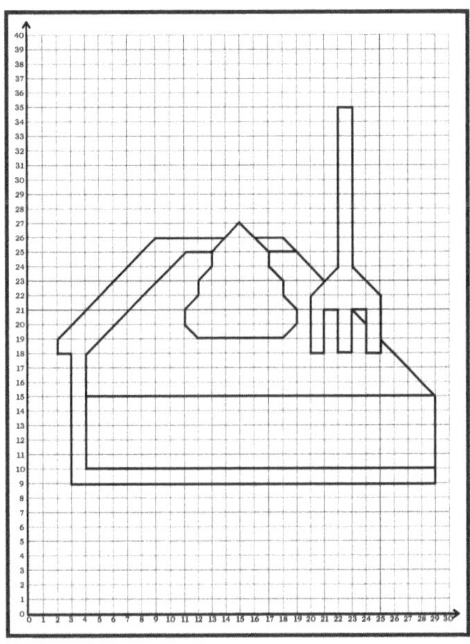

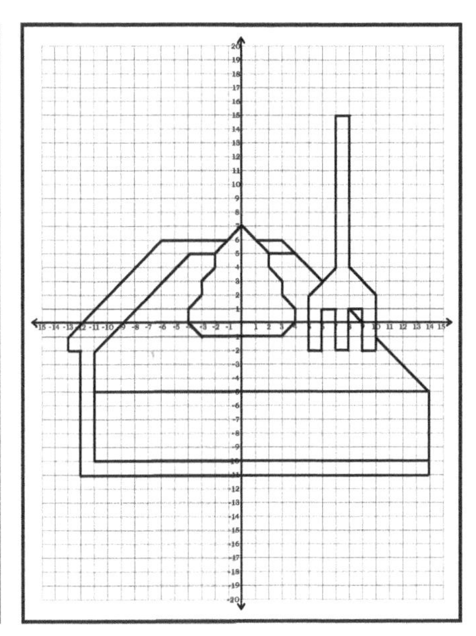

THANKSGIVING MYSTERY PICTURE #2

PAGE 99

PAGE 101

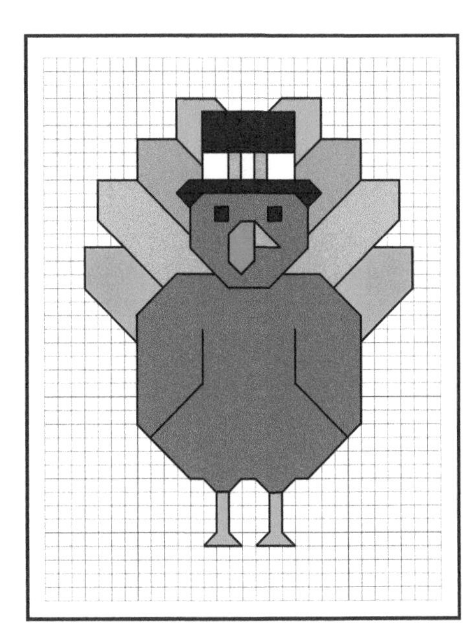

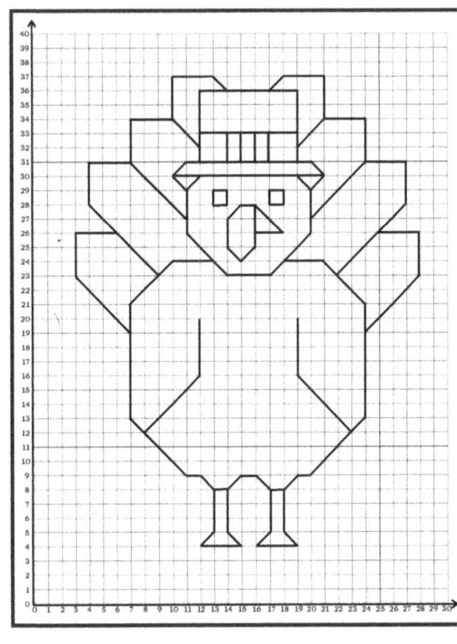

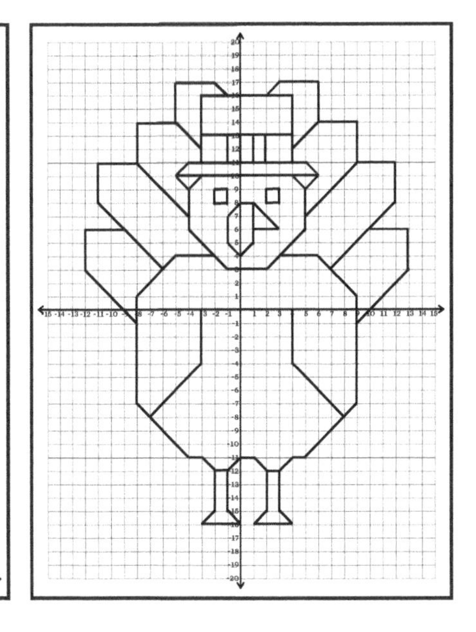

CHRISTMAS MYSTERY PICTURE #1

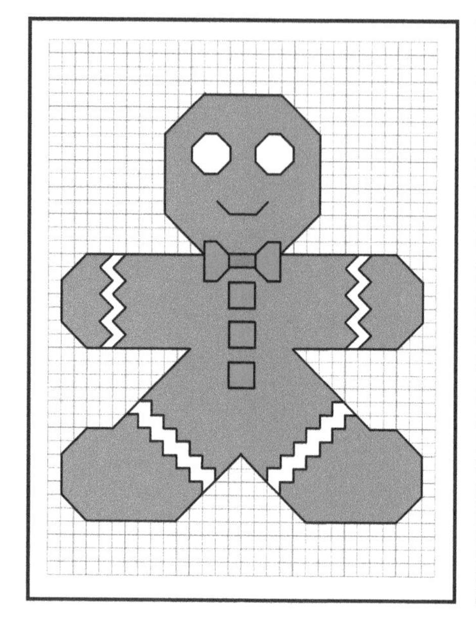

PAGE 103

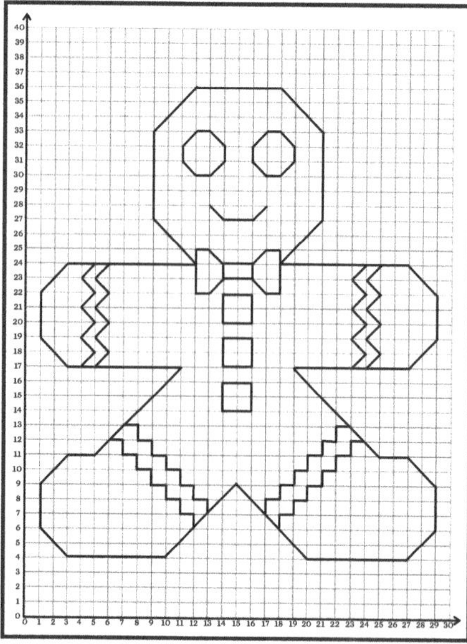

PAGE 105

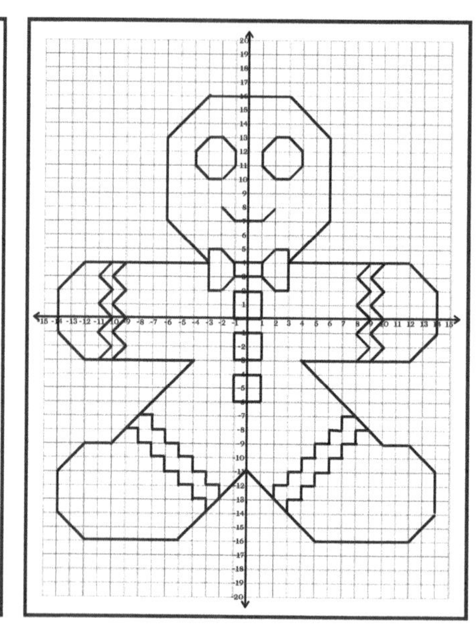

CHRISTMAS MYSTERY PICTURE #2

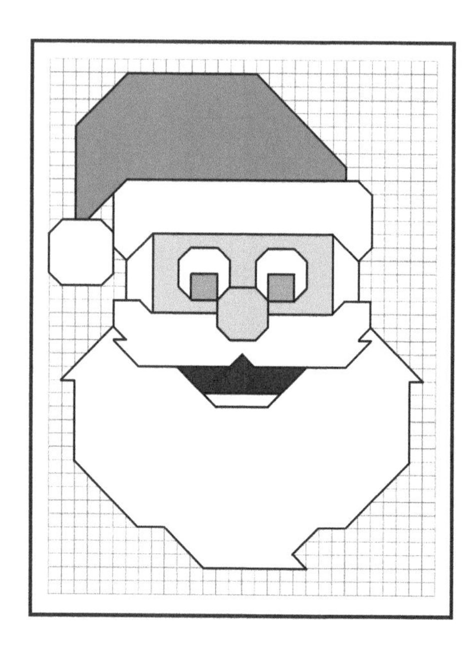

PAGE 107

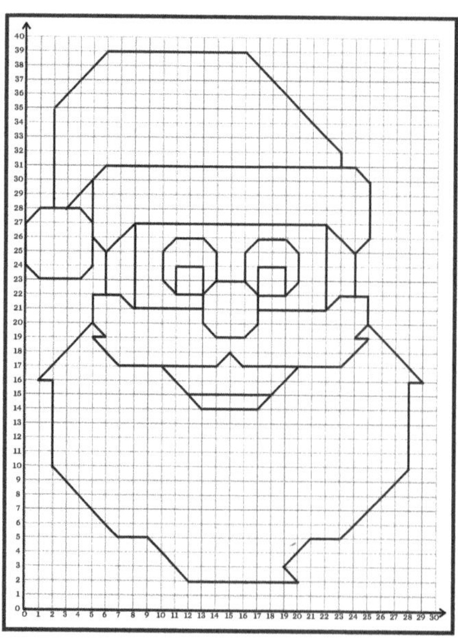

PAGE 109

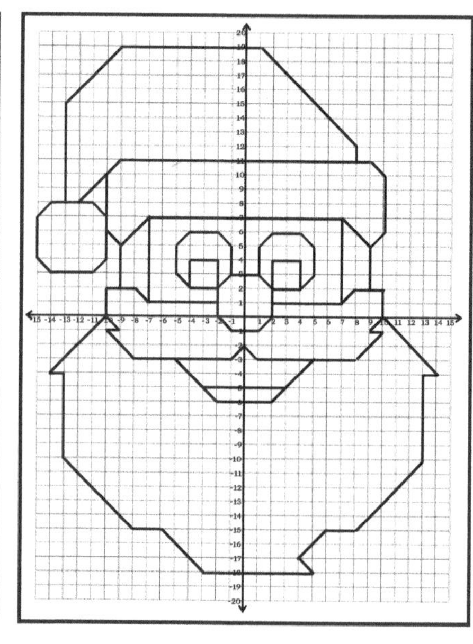

About the Authors

This book was created by Didi DeBoer & Meg Pfent, a mother-daughter duo with a passion for learning and education.

Didi DeBoer has a Masters Degree in Education and is a 20 year educator, teaching grades 1 - 8 before becoming a principal. She loves teaching math and making it fun for her students. These Mystery Coordinate Graph pictures were designed for her students who love completing them and often ask for more. Didi lives in Michigan with her family and Goldendoodle, Riley, who was one of the inspirations for the Puppy Pals section of this book. Enjoy!

Meg Pfent has a MBA from Wake Forest, and is a blogger, and writer. Meg lives in California with her husband and two Goldendoodles, Founder and Trooper, Their silly antics helped inspire Puppy Pals.